Tyranids

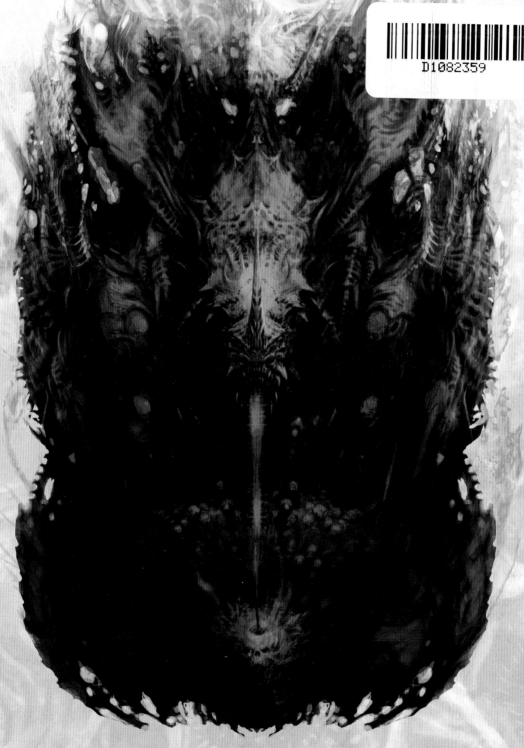

THE GREAT DEVOURER,
THE DESTROYER OF WORLDS,
THE SWARM OF THE HIVE MIND

CONTENTS

PRODUCED BY THE GAMES WORKSHOP DESIGN STUDIO

Thanks to our playtesters: Nick Bayton, John Bracken, Stefano Carlini, Paul Hickey, Matt Hilton, Trevor Larkin, Jim Lister.

UK	NORTHERN EUROPE	NORTH AMERICA	AUSTRALIA
Games Workshop Ltd,	Games Workshop Ltd,	Games Workshop Inc,	Games Workshop,
Willow Rd, Lenton,	Willow Rd, Lenton,	6211 East Holmes Road,	23 Liverpool Street,
Nottingham,	Nottingham,	Memphis,	Ingleburn,
NG7 2WS	NG7 2WS	Tennessee 38141	NSW 2565

INTRODUCTION

The Tyranids are an ancient race of hyper-aggressive aliens; a vast swarm of predators biologically adapted to kill and consume. Against such a consummate foe, even the mightiest of armies are naught but prey for the slaughter.

The Tyranids are a race of ravenously hungry aliens. They have travelled through the cold darkness of the intergalactic void, hibernating for aeons in order to feed upon the planets of our galaxy. Now they have awakened, sinking their tendrils ever deeper into populated space like a galactic plague of locusts. Impossibly large swarms of scuttling creatures, winged horrors and towering monstrosities consume everything in their path, scouring whole worlds of life as they seek to slake an insatiable appetite. The Tyranid race continuously learns and adapts, spawning new warriors and beasts of war to better defeat its foes. Unrelenting and unstoppable, the Tyranids represent an unimaginable threat, not only to Mankind, but to the whole galaxy.

WARHAMMER 40,000

If you are reading this codex, then you have already taken your first steps into the Warhammer 40,000 hobby. The Warhammer 40,000 rulebook contains all the rules you need to fight battles with your Citadel miniatures, and every army has its own codex that acts as a definitive guide to collecting and using it upon the tabletop battlefields of the Warhammer 40,000 universe. This codex allows you to turn your collection of Tyranids into an unstoppable swarm, ready to consume the galaxy.

TYRANIDS

Of all the races in the 41st Millennium, the Tyranids are the most alien. Each Tyranid is a living weapon, a creature perfectly designed to fulfil its role. Driven by the gestalt consciousness of the Hive Mind, the Tyranids overwhelm their prey with weight of numbers. Those that are not swept aside under a tide of razor-sharp claws and lethal bio-weaponry fire are smashed asunder by gigantic alien monsters the size of battle tanks.

HOW THIS CODEX WORKS

Codex: Tyranids contains everything you need to collect a force of Tyranids and devour your enemies in your games of Warhammer 40,000. Within these pages, you will find the history of the Tyranids since they first invaded the galaxy and the desperate battles that have ensued as their inexorable encroachment has pushed into the realms of other races. This book also contains rules for all the creatures and monsters at your disposal, as well as an army list that enables you to organise your collection of Citadel miniatures into a horde of the Hive Mind's warrior-organisms. Finally, you will find a showcase displaying beautifully painted miniatures from the Tyranids range, presenting the colour schemes of some of the most famous Tyranid hive fleets to have invaded the galaxy.

THE GREAT DEVOURER

The Tyranids are unlike any other race to be encountered by humanity. They are the ultimate predators, and all living things, from the lowliest insect to the most advanced civilisation, are nothing but their prey. Only now are the inhabitants of the galaxy realising the scale of the threat; unless the Tyranids can be stopped, it will mean nothing less than the extinction of all.

The Tyranids are likened to a galactic swarm consuming everything in its path, feeding on entire worlds and leaving only dead husks in their wake. Their threat is such that an unprotected planet can be infested and stripped clean of all its organic material in a matter of weeks without even slowing down the greater advance of the hive fleet.

THE INTERGALACTIC PREDATOR

The Tyranids are not native to our galaxy; they have journeyed here by traversing the unspeakable cold of intergalactic space, where time and space conspire to hold galaxies apart with inconceivable distances. Yet the Tyranids have crossed this space nonetheless, moving through the empty darkness for countless millennia to reach the rim of our galaxy. Who can say for sure what could compel an entire race to make such an epic venture? Perhaps the Tyranids have already consumed everything of worth in their home galaxy and must find new feeding grounds or starve. It is possible that the Tyranids have been preying on galaxies since time immemorial and ours is but the latest to feel their predations. Some have even speculated that the Tyranids are in flight from an even greater threat, be it a galactic disaster or another fearsome race, and have risked the nothingness between galaxies rather than face extinction. Whatever the truth, for the Tyranids to have endured such a voyage must have required utter single-mindedness and unimaginable energy. During their journey, the Tyranids slumbered in a state of frozen hibernation, but now they have arrived, they have awoken and they are hungry.

THE HIVE FLEETS

The Tyranids are a space-borne race that have inveigled their way into the realms of Man, as well as those of other xenos, like a disease spreading through a healthy body. The Tyranids travel in great fleets of gigantic living creatures that serve as spacecraft, each of which is home to countless lesser Tyranid organisms grown in the bubbling organ-sacs of the vessel's reproductive chambers. All of these creatures are born to serve the single entity that is the ship, and the ship itself exists only as part of the entity that is the hive fleet.

When a hive fleet encounters a prey world, it does not invade for territorial gain or out of a sense of pride or vengeance. Indeed, it is doubtful the Tyranids even comprehend such concepts. Rather, they invade to harvest valuable biomass and feed their insatiable hunger. The Tyranids require an endless supply of food, not only to nourish the hive fleets, but to grow new organisms. Therefore, when a hive fleet invades a planet rich in life, every action of every Tyranid creature is honed to a single goal – the total and rapid absorption of that world's population, ecosystems and bio-resources. To this end, the hive fleet creates an army with the express purpose of overcoming the prey world's defenders before the planet is stripped of every scrap of biomatter and devoured.

CREATURES OF THE SWARM

Tyranid warrior-organisms are creatures of visceral horror, implacable monsters with razor-sharp claws, which can tear a man apart in the blink of an eye, and grotesque bio-cannons that fire hungry, parasitic projectiles into their prey's flesh.

Every weapon and projectile used by the hive fleets is a living organism, grown from the reconstituted biomatter of previous invasions. The Tyranids have no form of mechanical technology and, instead, harness an advanced form of biotechnology to create organic equivalents of the tools, weaponry and ammunition used by other races. These creatures live in a highly symbiotic fashion, fusing into each other's flesh so that it is often impossible to say where one Tyranid creature ends, and another begins. In this way, Tyranid warrior-beasts wield living weapons that are literally extensions of their own bodies, each one a killing machine, perfectly adapted to slaughter its victims.

The bio-construct nature of the Tyranids makes them a terrible foe to face, for their armies contain a creature specialised for every conceivable facet of warfare, which can be altered and re-grown to suit a battle's needs in a short span of time. Thus can a hive fleet adapt to generate a force capable of overwhelming any opposition, unleashing a vast throng of ferocious alien monsters that can fly, run, burrow and stalk through the defences of any foe.

THE HIVE MIND

The Magos Biologis of the Imperium categorises each Tyranid hive fleet as a separate force, an individual entity that competes with other hive fleets for resources. Indeed, each is self-sufficient, appearing to exhibit different strategies and developing unique creatures to overcome its prey. However, the truth is more complex, for each hive fleet is but a splinter of one greater assemblage. The Tyranids' numbers are vast beyond counting, swarms so large that they block out the very stars, yet each and every creature is but a single cell in the living body of a single super-organism.

Every thought and action, every spark of life in the Tyranid race, is bound and interlinked into a single unfathomable consciousness, a great entity that stretches across hundreds of light years of space. This gestalt sentience is known as the Hive Mind. It holds all Tyranids in a psychic bond that enables them to act together in perfect unison. Under the influence of this ancient consciousness, the Tyranids have fed on countless planets and devoured civilisations since time immemorial.

The majority of Tyranid organisms have no distinct minds as a human would understand it, having been created to perform a single task to the exclusion of all else. Unless the implacable will of the Hive Mind instructs them to do otherwise, these organisms simply fulfil the functions for which they were created, acting on nothing more than instinct. Larger, more complicated, Tyranid beasts have been grown to make limited decisions appropriate to current stimuli and situations, but even these actions are subordinate to the goals of the Hive Mind.

The Hive Mind's influence is strongest in the vicinity of creatures such as Tyranid Warriors and the feared Hive Tyrants. These beings are able to communicate with their kin, not through language, but by a synaptic form of telepathy through which they relay and channel the will of the Hive Mind. Under the command of such creatures, the Tyranids operate in perfect unison, slaved to the psychic imperatives of a single communal intelligence. However, should the synapse creatures be slain, the link between individual creatures and the Hive Mind will be severed – many of the lesser organisms will revert to their baser, animalistic behaviours. For this reason, the Tyranid swarms do not have only a single commander, but many, to ensure the Hive Mind's synaptic control is maintained across the entire Tyranid race.

THE SHADOW IN THE WARP

The coming of a Tyranid hive fleet is preceded by a smothering psychic signal that envelops entire star systems and disrupts all forms of Warp travel and communication. Swallowed up by psychic-static, whole worlds suddenly go deathly silent, giving no clues as to what is unfolding on the surface below, or of what terrors are about to befall. This is the Shadow in the Warp, and it heralds imminent invasion and horror.

It is unknown if the Shadow in the Warp is created deliberately by the hive fleets, or if it is simply a by-product of the Hive Mind's innate synaptic control. In any case, the Shadow in the Warp creates fear and panic wherever it falls, instilling a pervasive dread into the minds of a prey world's defenders, plunging entire planets into misery and despair. For highly psychic races, such as the Eldar, or for luckless psykers caught within this enervating effect, the malaise is magnified tenfold. Should a psyker attempt to use his otherworldly abilities, the cerebral cacophony worsens even further; the psychic sound of a billion alien thoughts scratch at his mind, and unless he is particularly strong-willed he will be pitched into an insanity where he will repeatedly utter phrases in a tongue too alien to properly pronounce.

For races such as the Imperium of Man, whose means of interstellar communication and travel rely upon highly specialised psykers such as Astropaths and Navigators, the Shadow in the Warp is one of the deadliest facets of the Tyranid menace. Bereft of their means to call for reinforcements or safely navigate surrounding space, the worlds of the Imperium are easily isolated from the wider galaxy. This means that, by the time the Shadow in the Warp falls, it is already too late; these beleaguered planets are effectively on their own. They must fend for themselves and face the Tyranid swarm with the weapons they have to hand, or die in the attempt.

DESTROYER OF WORLDS

The Tyranids do not communicate with other races, and why should they do so? Tyranids are as far above other life forms, such as Mankind, as Mankind is above the domesticated livestock it consumes. The Tyranids cannot be reasoned with, appeased or surrendered to. There can be no hope of mercy from such a foe. To face the Tyranids is simply a matter of survival: kill or be consumed.

So far, the Tyranids have been devouring worlds in the Eastern Fringe, feasting on the very borders of the Imperium. But with every passing year, the hive fleets push deeper into regions of populated space whilst still more approach from the intergalactic void and emerge from their aeons-long slumbers. The thought processes of the Hive Mind are gathering pace as more Tyranids wake and recall the age-old purpose of their kind – feed, grow, survive.

'There is a cancer eating at the Imperium. With each decade it advances deeper, leaving drained, dead worlds in its wake. This horror, this abomination, has thought and purpose which functions on an unimaginable, galactic scale, and all we can do is try to stop the swarms of bio-engineered monsters it unleashes upon us by instinct. We have given the horror a name to salve our fears; we call it the Tyranid race, but if it is aware of us at all, it must know us only as Prey.'

– Inquisitor Czevak at the Conclave of Har

FIRST CONTACT

Mankind's first recorded contact with Tyranids happened in early 745.M41, on the eastern outskirts of the Imperium. Up to this point, Mankind was wholly unaware of the new threat on its borders, and if any of the galaxy's older empires knew of the oncoming swarm, they did not see fit to warn the upstart Imperium.

For decades, since their arrival on the galactic rim, the hive fleets had consumed worlds with no intelligent life, replenishing the reserves of biomatter expended during the long, slow crawl through the interstellar void. Now reinvigorated, the aliens descended upon the far-flung Imperial world of Tyran Primus – an invasion for which the Imperium would thereafter name their race: Tyranids.

Tyran Primus was home to a heavily fortified Adeptus Mechanicus explorator outpost and was no easy prey. Given the outpost's position on the very edge of known space, and its separation from the Imperium's other worlds, it had been founded with both a garrison and armaments deemed adequate to deter the attentions of both piratical raiders and alien invasion. Four giant defence lasers stood guard over the Tyran Primus main base, each protected by void shield generators. This formidable firepower was complemented by an overlapping network of macro-cannon strongpoints, defence bastions and Icarus weapon emplacements. Nor was the planetary garrison lacking in strength. In addition to the Skitarii bodyguard of the outpost's commander, Magos Varnak, Tyran boasted three Endeavour-class space cruisers and an entire infantry regiment of the Imperial Guard. Such was a standard force for a frontier outpost of the Imperium, a design that had proven itself against a hundred adversaries. Yet here, against this new alien menace, this formidable arsenal would be sorely tested.

THE ASSAULT BEGINS

Tyran's defence lasers opened fire the moment the first bio-ships made orbit. The planet's storm-wracked skies were split again and again by incandescent blasts as the base's gunners desperately fended off the descending invaders. Then, just as the cooling systems of the defence lasers began to overheat, the invaders withdrew. Perhaps buoyed by false confidence, Magos Varnak ordered his small fleet to harry the withdrawing vessels, but this strategy soon proved folly. Penetrating the thick spore cloud that masked the alien fleet, the pursuing vessels discovered that fewer than a dozen bio-ships had been destroyed out of a fleet of several thousand. Having lured the cruisers away from Tyran, the hive fleet hungrily fell upon the Imperial vessels. The ancient cruisers lasted long enough to convey a warning to the Tyran outpost before leech-like pods gnawed through their hulls, unleashing hundreds of hungry aliens directly into their decks. The crew were slaughtered within minutes, leaving the doomed cruisers adrift in space.

When the hive fleet returned to Tyran, the defence lasers could not hold the bio-ships back. Thousands of invaders descended on the world, and though the planet's fortifications destroyed many, countless other warrior-organisms made it through the net of fire to reach Tyran Primus' surface. Within the hour, the first invaders reached the base's walls.

THE DEATH OF TYRAN

Imperial Guard officers bellowed orders through the pouring rain, and in response, torrents of firepower scythed into the alien ranks. At first, the disciplined volleys drove the creatures back. Wave after wave of creatures were blasted apart, their corpses choking the rain-lashed kill zones between the bastions. Then, the northern defence laser fell silent; flocks of bat-winged horrors had thrown themselves into its throat, their own charred corpses clogging the massive weapon. Moments later, the eastern defence laser ceased firing as a towering alien giant of chitin and muscle rammed through its walls, trampled over its gunnery crew and demolished its coolant lines. One by one, the outpost's defences fell, and there was no way to hold back the next wave of attackers.

In moments, thousands of aliens were rampaging through the outpost, destroying everything in reach. The base's last defensive fortifications were swiftly overrun and the Imperial Guardsmen within butchered. Whilst a few pockets of resistance still held out under the watchful gaze of a Commissar, these were vastly outnumbered, surrounded, and quickly torn apart. Only Magos Varnak's command bunker remained; its ceramite walls cracking and its adamantium gate buckling under the impact of massive alien claws. Finally, the great gate crashed inwards and fanged nightmares poured into the breach in its wake. A few remaining Skitarii fought back with flamers, but the aliens swarmed through the searing fires and hacked their way onwards. Varnak knew that escape was impossible. All that remained was to warn the Imperium before selling his life as dearly as possible.

Unable to transmit a message by means of astrotelepathy, the aliens having cut off all psychic communication, Varnak compiled a data-codex containing Tyran's records. With only seconds left, Varnak shot the codex plummeting into space before whispering a final prayer and activating the sacred self-destruct rune of ending, annihilating the entire outpost in a cataclysmic plasma explosion.

Tyran Primus was lost. The First Tyrannic War had begun.

> *'We cannot live through this. Mankind cannot live through this. In a single day, they have covered this planet with a flood of living blades and needle-fanged mouths. Kill one, and ten take its place. If they are truly without number, then our race is doomed to a violent death before every shred of our civilisation is scoured away by a force more voracious than the fires of hell themselves.*
>
> *Death! By the Machine God, Death is here!'*
> - MAGOS VARNAK, LAST WORDS

PHASE IV: ASSIMILATION

Having gorged themselves, the Tyranid feeder-organisms return to large digestion pools where both they, and the biomatter they have devoured, are dissolved into a rich biological gruel that is funnelled up through vast capillary towers and absorbed by the Tyranid's orbiting bio-ships. When the culling is complete and every shred of biomatter is assimilated, the Tyranids move on in search of fresh feeding grounds, leaving a scoured, lifeless wasteland behind.

PHASE III: CONSUMPTION

Once a prey world's defenders have been defeated, writhing tides of feeder-organisms are unleashed to cover the planet, consuming every scrap of flesh, every blade of vegetation and every drop of moisture. Nothing is left to waste, especially not the corpses littering the battlefields of the prey world. Whether these are the bodies of slain defenders or the remains of fallen Tyranids, all are consumed so that its biomatter may be recycled and the hive fleet replenished.

PHASE II: PREDATION

As the swarms flood across the landscape, slaughtering the planet's inhabitants like cattle, strange alien structures begin to grow on the surface, which start poisoning the world's ecosystems. The Tyranids respond to threats with overwhelming numbers, expending lives by the millions to ensure all opposition is removed. If this fails, the hive fleet creates fresh new waves of Tyranids, which are each specifically adapted to overcome any defences that remain.

PHASE I: INVASION

When a hive fleet locates a suitable prey world, it descends to the planet and disgorges a swarm of creatures into its ecosystem. Hordes of Tyranid vanguard warrior-organisms make planetfall and churn across the world's surface, driven by the impulse to feed. The skies turn red as Tyranid spores choke the atmosphere. They then blacken as clouds of winged horrors dive from above. Soon, the prey world is seething with Tyranid creatures.

THE BEHEMOTH

Having scoured Tyran Primus of biomass, the alien hive fleet moved on in search of other worlds to feed upon, pushing its tendrils ever deeper into the galaxy whilst the death screams of an entire world went unheard.

Were it not for a single man – Inquisitor Kryptman – the fate of Tyran might have gone entirely unnoticed. After all, the galaxy is a big place, mysteries are commonplace and the Imperium is as slow to react as only a monolithic bureaucracy can be. Whilst in time many other Inquisitors, including such distinguished names as Czevak, Agmar and Lok, would come to realise the true threat of the Hive Mind, were it not for Kryptman, its very existence would not have been known before it was already too late. Indeed, whether through a quirk of fate or out of some investigative instinct, Kryptman's decision to personally investigate Tyran's mysterious silence proved vital to the Imperium's survival.

A Grim Discovery

By the time Kryptman reached Tyran, a year had passed since the attack. At first, the Inquisitor could not equate the husk of a planet he found to ocean-bound Tyran Primus. The world had been sucked dry; every scrap of vegetation and every drop of water was gone. A crater was all that remained of the Adeptus Mechanicus outpost, and all that could be found of the planet's cruiser fleet were acid-eaten hulks; icy shells devoid of life and adrift in space. After a long search, Inquisitor Kryptman recovered Magos Varnak's data-codex, the knowledge contained within it bought with the life of an entire planet. What Kryptman saw when he reviewed the fragmented data was a dire prophesy of doom; static-laced images of scythe-limbed aliens, footage of the skies over Tyran turning black with swarming monsters, and orbital pict-views of a fleet of living ships so vast that the stellar horizon was veiled in inky blackness. Kryptman felt hollow as he realised what he had discovered. Not wasting another moment, the Inquisitor set forth to warn the galaxy of the oncoming horror from beyond the stars, a horror he named 'Tyranids' for the doomed world they had consumed.

Kryptman ordered his Astropath to send a warning to the Imperium, but the psyker could not penetrate the Warp turmoil left by the passing of the alien fleet. Even the nearby Thandros telepathica booster matrix was obscured. In desperation, Kryptman set course for Thandros in the hopes of re-establishing communications with the Imperium there.

The Fate of Thandros

It was on this voyage that Kryptman realised the scale of the Tyranid threat. Following in the hive fleet's wake, Kryptman discovered a string of barren worlds that records indicated should be verdant and lush. Reviewing a decade's worth of planetary survey data, Kryptman saw a pattern emerging. He was able to plot the hive fleet's course by the trail of dead and lifeless worlds it had left behind. There was no subtlety to the hive fleet's approach, no sense of strategic genius. It merely ploughed through the galaxy without stopping, devouring everything in its path with a rapacious hunger that would become its defining feature. As dictated by tradition, Kryptman codified the new alien threat with an ancient and forbidding name from legend: Behemoth.

Though Kryptman's ship made good speed, the Tyranids had attacked the Thandros system and moved on long before his arrival. Thandros was not as well protected as Tyran, and was similarly unable to hold back the swarms of Tyranid horrors that railed against them. The telepathica matrix was found to have emptied all of its turret magazines and burned out its defence laser crystal before being overrun. Thandros had fought bravely, but its populace had been slaughtered.

A Voice in the Dark

With Thandros lost, Kryptman's quest became critical. The next system in Behemoth's path was Ultramar, and unless forewarned, the Imperium might lose its best chance to stand against the Tyranid onslaught. With haste, Kryptman salvaged the telepathica matrix and through a herculean effort, his Astropath finally managed to pierce the Shadow in the Warp to contact the unsuspecting Imperium. The Astropath, nose and ears bleeding from the effort, broadcast Kryptman's warning. One voice spoke back from the dark, and it came from Macragge, the heart of Ultramar and the home world of the Ultramarines Chapter of Space Marines.

The Ultramarines had heard Inquisitor Kryptman's call, but the message was garbled and incomplete. The Space Marines knew that a dire threat was approaching, but they did not fully understand the true nature of their foe. Knowing he would have to deliver his report in person, Kryptman set course for Macragge. The Navigator of Kryptman's ship strained to follow the guiding light of the Astronomican through the swirling energies of Warp space. At times, the undertow left by Hive Fleet Behemoth threatened to lose the Inquisitor's ship in the Warp, but the Navigator avoided every whirlpool and riptide with consummate skill, and Kryptman somehow arrived at Macragge ahead of Hive Fleet Behemoth.

Inquisitor Kryptman met with Marneus Calgar, Chapter Master of the Ultramarines, beneath the portico of his white marble palace. Calgar stood as a giant before the Inquisitor, his stature grand even among the superhuman warriors of the Space Marines. Calgar listened intently, but Kryptman's terrible discoveries did not disturb his noble demeanour. Nothing escaped Calgar's notice, not one detail about the foe that could be turned into an advantage. Hive Fleet Behemoth was fast approaching, and the Ultramarines Chapter prepared for the greatest battle in their history.

> *'An alien threat has risen from beyond the abyss, a swarm so vast that it blots out the stars. This horror fights neither for power nor territory, but rather to feed a hunger so insatiable that it will eventually devour the entire galaxy.'*
>
> – Inquisitor Kryptman

TYRANID BIO-SHIPS

Tyranid bio-ships are enormous space-swimming creatures, whose grotesque forms are endless in variety and function. No bio-ship is truly a single organism; rather, each is a complex composite of dozens, if not hundreds, of different creatures. Every part, every organ and extremity, is a specifically designed bio-construct operating under the single, unified consciousness of the bio-ship itself.

The largest bio-ships dwarf even the battleships of the Imperial Navy. Their outer skins are pocked with meteor craters, and grasping tentacles the length of hive-spires seek out morsels to consume; enemy ships caught within their grasp are doomed to be broken apart and rammed into impossibly vast, churning maws. Nor are bio-ships defenceless at range, for many possess giant bio-cannons that spit gouts of acid and other, stranger projectiles across the vacuum, debilitating their prey before closing for the kill.

Many Tyranid ships are incredibly old, having travelled through the intergalactic void for aeons. Moving together in great shoals, bio-ships hibernate as they traverse space. The vast majority of Tyranid organisms within a ship's cavernous innards also lie in a dormant state – thousands of warrior-creatures are incubated within pods that line the vessel's

reproductive chambers. These sleeping horrors are but a defence force, maintained in case the bio-ship comes under attack. A small number of sentry creatures scuttle through the bio-ship's arterial passageways, searching for invaders like an immune system. If any should be found, a telepathic signal is sent that awakens their kin from their slumber. A foe foolish enough to board a Tyranid bio-ship will soon find itself overwhelmed by a flood of frenzied Tyranids whose only thought is the protection of the ship.

Aside from the sentries, the only other creatures moving around within the miles of arterial passages and tubes that make up a Tyranid bio-ship are lesser creatures that perform mindless, repetitive duties to keep the ship healthy during its long passage. Some exist purely to eat away unwanted growths and dead tissues, others to transport fluids from one part of the ship to another, a few to feed strange organs whose functions defy all understanding. It is only once the hive fleet nears a prey world that the bio-ship stirs to full wakefulness. The Hive Mind's influence spreads through the ship and individual organs jolt into life in response. The bio-ship begins to create thousands, if not millions more warrior-organisms in preparation for the invasion, digestive tracts the size of cities grumbling in anticipation of the feast to come.

BATTLE FOR MACRAGGE

When Hive Fleet Behemoth arrived at Macragge, the Tyranids found it fortified against them. This was no isolated frontier world, neither was it an ill-defended relay system to be overwhelmed in a brief but vicious struggle. This was Macragge, the Imperium's bulwark on the eastern rim and home world to an entire Chapter of Space Marines.

Thanks to Inquisitor Kryptman, Macragge had been warned of the Tyranids, and Marneus Calgar bent his legendary strategic skills to buttressing Macragge's already formidable defences. Space Marine Strike Cruisers and Battle Barges loomed like gigantic azure monoliths amongst the Ultramar Defence Fleet and the planet's orbital weapon platforms; Macragge was surrounded with a ring of firepower. Another foe would have been daunted by the assemblage of might that now guarded the capital world of Ultramar, but the Tyranids came on without delay. The first waves of bio-ships swept past the defences, intent on reaching the planet below. Each vessel was targeted and eliminated in turn by massed firepower, but not before delivering clusters of bio-organisms to Macragge's surface.

Tyranids swarmed over the planet's frozen landscape, and the Ultramarines were quick to respond. For a time, Calgar's forces slowed the tide, trading territory for time as they whittled down the oncoming swarm, dividing the rampaging hordes and staining the snow with alien ichor. Yet even under Calgar's leadership, such tactics could only last for so long against such numbers, and the Ultramarines were soon forced into making a stand at Cold Steel Ridge.

THE SWARMLORD STRIKES

The Hive Mind had learnt from the Ultramarines' tactics, and having identified Calgar as the main threat to the Tyranid advance, it unleashed its deadliest servant to bring about his end – the Hive Tyrant later classified in Imperial records as the 'Swarmlord'. Under the influence of the Swarmlord, the Tyranids' primal fury was coupled with keen strategy. Instead of mindlessly charging at their prey, the Tyranids circumvented fire zones, ambushed enemy counter-attacks and concentrated on weak points in Calgar's line that could only have been perceived by a military genius. The Ultramarines were in danger of being overwhelmed.

With the foe reeling, the Swarmlord extended its will and ten thousand alien minds answered. Raveners and Trygons burst from the chill ground in the midst of manned trenches, forming a wall of writhing bodies that separated the beleaguered defenders from Calgar's main force. By the time the Ultramarines cut through the subterranean swarms, the trench network was a charnel of gore overrun with Tyranids. The Ultramarines purged them with fire, but in so doing left the Swarmlord's true target – the mighty Baneblade *Pride of Hera* – without infantry support. A wave of Carnifexes tore the super-heavy tank apart and with its destruction, the western flank was lost.

On the eastern flank, Calgar cursed himself for underestimating his foe. Under the Swarmlord's dominion, the swarm was adapting to defeat Calgar's tactics as quickly as he could conceive them. Knowing that staying on Cold Steel Ridge would waste more lives, Calgar ordered his forces to fall back to the orbiting Battle Barge *Octavius*. All the Ultramarines needed to do was to hold out long enough for Thunderhawk Gunships to arrive and extract them.

Somehow, the Swarmlord sensed Calgar's intent to escape, and with an alien shriek, it plunged into the fray. Beside the Swarmlord came a host of elite warrior-organisms, and together they cut a path directly towards their quarry. Seeing the danger heading towards their Chapter Master, the Ultramarines hastened to his aid but found themselves assailed from all sides as the Swarmlord urged hordes of lesser creatures to intercept the would-be heroes. The swarm fell upon the Ultramarines with blind fury, undaunted by the roar of boltguns. Their deaths did little more than delay the Space Marines, but it would prove enough; Calgar would have to face the Swarmlord and its bodyguard alone.

Calgar fought like a hero of legend, but there were simply too many foes and he was finally laid low, his body rent and torn. Calgar's last strength was expended in mortal combat with the Swarmlord itself, and the Hive Tyrant towered over the Space Marine, blades raised to deliver the killing blow. But the fatal strike never fell. Redoubling their efforts, Calgar's Honour Guard broke through the mass of Tyranids to throw themselves in front of their wounded Chapter Master, axes of Ultramar flashing in the cold light as they slowly drove the Swarmlord back and shielded their lord with their own bodies. Through valour and sacrifice, they held the swarm back until the Thunderhawks arrived to evacuate the surviving Ultramarines. Marneus Calgar would not die this day, but Cold Steel Ridge was lost.

THE WAR IN SPACE

Yet if the battle on the ground fared poorly, the war in space was proving disastrous. The first Tyranid assault wave had claimed the mighty Battle Barge *Caesar*. The third wave saw the destruction of the better part of Ultramar's Defence Fleet. By the time the ninth wave was launched, Macragge's orbital defence stations were bloody tombs, mere hunks of debris left spinning in space. Macragge now lay undefended, and the Tyranid invasion intensified.

A fresh wave of bioforms landed on Macragge, bringing a new stage of the planetary assault directly to the prey world's polar fortresses. However, the war in space was not yet concluded. Refusing all but the most vital medical aid, Calgar took command of the remaining ships and turned their firepower to the orbiting hive fleet. The Hive Mind responded as it had done before at Tyran Primus, withdrawing its bio-vessels from the planet to lure the prey

world's defending fleet into a deadly trap. Calgar took the bait, and pursued the hive fleet to the ringed world of Circe on the edge of the Macragge System, but not without a plan of his own.

As Calgar approached Circe, a second shoal of bio-ships concealed in the planet's rings launched themselves at the battered fleet. However, the first salvoes had scarcely been exchanged when Battlefleet Tempestus entered real space on the far side of Circe – it was the Tyranids' turn to be caught in the jaws of a trap. Even so, the fighting was fierce, and only the desperate sacrifice of the *Dominus Astra* swung the battle in the Imperium's favour, the great Emperor class battleship detonating its mighty Warp engines and creating a cataclysmic vortex that dragged many hive ships to oblivion. Caught between the guns of two Imperial fleets, the remaining bio-ships were destroyed soon after.

THE BEHEMOTH FALLS

In truth, Hive Fleet Behemoth was defeated at Circe. The only question that remained was whether Macragge would be lost in the process. Whilst battle raged in space, the valour of the Ultramarines was being tested as never before on the surface. The veterans of the 1st Company led a tenacious defence of the polar fortresses, holding every wall and battlement. When their boltguns ran dry, the Space Marines switched to their pistols; when they too ran out of ammunition, they fought with chainswords, combat blades or even bare fists, but not once did they yield. Only at the last possible moment did the veterans fall back to their fortresses' hearts, prepared to sell their lives dearly.

When the fleet-bound Ultramarines returned to Macragge, they found a landscape subsumed by carnage. Though a few survivors were found in the ruin of Macragge's southern fortress, none were discovered in the north. The 1st Company had died there to a man, fighting back-to-back against the full fury of the swarm, their bodies swamped amongst mounds of the Tyranid dead. Though the Ultramarines had defeated Behemoth, they had been dealt a blow that would take centuries to recover from.

The body of a Hive Tyrant believed to be the Swarmlord was found on the corpse-littered ice fields outside the northern polar fortress, but the damage it had sustained made it impossible to identify with certainty. Rumours persist that the beast had somehow escaped death and that the Tyranids would one day return. It would be decades before the truth was revealed.

> 'As I looked into its dead black eyes, I saw the terrible sentience it had in place of a soul. Behind that was the steel will of its leader. Further still, I could feel its primogenitor coldly assessing me from the void. And looking back from the deepest recesses of the alien's mind, I perceived what I can describe only as an immortal hunger.
>
> 'We can slay the Tyranids on our worlds, blast their fleets from space, grind their armies to torn and ruined fragments. But their hunger? That is beyond our ability to slay.'
> - VARRO TIGURIUS, ULTRAMARINES CHIEF LIBRARIAN

The First Tyrannic War

589.M41 The Sin of Damnation
The Genestealer-infested space hulk, *Sin of Damnation*, is cleansed in a close-fought series of assaults by the Blood Angels 1st Company. At the time, none are aware that the Genestealers are the vanguard of an imminent galactic invasion.

c. 730.M41 The Behemoth Arrives
A vast fleet of alien bio-ships enters the galaxy on the Eastern Fringe.

739.M41 The Flight of Malan'tai
Warned of the Tyranid onslaught by far-flung bands of Rangers, the Farseers of Craftworld Malan'tai opt to remove themselves from Behemoth's approach whilst there is still time to escape.

745.M41 The Death of Tyran

746.M41 Kryptman's Quest
Whilst investigating the mysterious silence of Tyran Primus, Inquisitor Kryptman learns the horror of the alien threat. Kryptman names the aliens 'Tyranids' and races to warn to the Imperium.

c. 746.M41 The Thandros Incident
The binary worlds of Thandros offer little resistance to the oncoming Tyranids and their citizens are slaughtered in the darkness of their own mines.

749.M41 Behemoth Advances
Imperial Explorator Fleet Dorsari, the world of Helmont and the Moons of Ra'pson all fall before Behemoth's inexorable advance.

c. 752.M41 The Jagga Waaagh!
Behemoth falls upon Jagga, pirate base of Kaptin Blackgit. The Ork Kroozers that form Blackgit's fleet launch boarding parties to storm the encroaching bio-ships. The tide soon turns when the rampaging Orks awaken the Tervigons within each ship, which spawn countless broods of Termagants. The Orks are swamped and the Termagants then flood back through the Orks' own boarding tubes to slaughter the Kroozers' crews. Blackgit, sensing defeat as the communications from his fleet abruptly end, attempts to escape by ramming his ship through a lone bio-vessel blocking his path, only to fatally discover it is a starship-sized spore mine.

752.M41 Prandium Devoured
Prandium, the jewel of Ultramar, proves an easy and bountiful conquest for the Tyranids. The barren rock left in Behemoth's wake is scarcely recognisable as the once verdant paradise of yore.

753.M41 The Sybari Slaughter
The Chaos Renegade warband known as the Death Shadows musters at Sybari in preparation for a secret strike against Ultramar. They are isolated when the Shadow in the Warp envelops the system, and their warlord, the Sorcerer Malafor, is driven to insanity by the Tyranids' psychic presence. Leaderless and in the midst of preparing for an assault of their own, the renegades are unprepared to defend Sybari from the swarm. Though they reap a high tally, the entire warband is annihilated in less than an hour.

754.M41 The Purge of Ymgarl
The Salamanders conduct a xenocidal campaign to purge the moons of Ymgarl of Genestealer infestation. Though the Salamanders suffer heavy casualties, the moons are finally declared scoured, or so they believe…

801-807.M41 A New Threat

Hive Fleet Naga, a relatively small Tyranid fleet, descends upon the Ybaric Cluster and consumes several minor races on the edge of Ulumeathi space. Its progress does not noticeably slow.

801-808.M41 A Cry for Help

A string of Eldar Exodite worlds and maiden worlds fall under the shadow of Hive Fleet Naga. The Eldar craftworlds of Idharae, Iyanden and Malan'tai despatch fleets to their aid.

809.M41 The Serpent Wounded

The leading elements of Hive Fleet Naga are caught between the warfleets of Idharae and Malan'tai. Naga splinters into two tendrils.

810-811.M41 The War for Halathel

The flagship of Iyanden's fleet is destroyed whilst attempting to pierce the Tyranid blockade on Halathel. Prince Yriel assumes command and defeats the remaining bio-ships, but it is too late to save Halathel's Exodite protectors. Overwhelmed by rage and grief, Yriel orders the planet to be scoured of all life lest a single Tyranid survive, before rushing to rejoin his kin at Eth-aelas.

206812.M41 Eth-aelas Besieged

Cornered and outgunned, the second, smaller tendril of Hive Fleet Naga is easily destroyed by Eldar pulsar fire, but not before its bio-ships seed Eth-aelas with warrior-beasts. The Eldar forces make planetfall to seek and destroy the remaining Tyranids on the surface.

459812.M41 The Sound of Doom

A psychic scream echoes through the caverns of the webway as all contact is lost with Craftworld Malan'tai.

860812.M41 Naga Defeated

Yriel's forces arrive at Eth-aelas and immediately join the Eldar already fighting on the planet's surface. After a string of bloody victories for the craftworlds' combined warhosts, the last Hive Tyrant is slain at the battle of Sorrowforge Pinnacle. The survivors of the swarm are left leaderless and easy prey for the vengeful Eldar. The majority of Hive Fleet Naga is destroyed, though there will be many further battles before all of its constituent parts are wiped out. The Eldar learn first hand the horror of the Tyranid race.

756.M41 Assault on Calth

Bio-ships seed Calth with invaders before rejoining the hive fleet at Circe. Though few in number, the Tyranids are led by a great Carnifex that wreaks havoc until it is shot in the skull by a Commissar.

757.M41 Battle for Macragge

Hive Fleet Behemoth reaches Macragge. There they face the entire Ultramarines Chapter, who ultimately seize a bloody victory. Behemoth is effectively destroyed.

789.M41 A Monster Reawakens

The body of a one-eyed Carnifex is discovered encased in ice on Calth. Though believed to be dead, the creature awakens and butchers everything in its path. Hundreds of Tyranid creatures that had been lurking in Calth's labyrinthine cave systems emerge and flock to the Carnifex's side. As tales of its rampage reach Macragge, the Ultramarines despatch Sergeant Telion to hunt down the monster terrorising Calth's populace, a beast they have entitled 'Old One Eye'.

820.M41 The Belly of the Beast

Mortifactors Space Marines board an isolated hive ship believed to have survived Behemoth's destruction. The Space Marines suffer ninety percent casualties, but eventually slay the giant bio-vessel.

850.M41 The Anphelion Project

An Imperial taskforce, sent to investigate a covert project which studied captured Tyranid life forms, is ambushed and decimated by monstrous alien organisms.

THE KRAKEN

For more than two hundred years after Hive Fleet Behemoth's rampage, the Imperium was relatively untroubled by the Tyranids. Though several smaller hive fleets passed into the galaxy in that time, they primarily vented their fury on alien worlds, leading many to believe the Tyranid menace was all but ended. Nothing could have been further from the truth.

By early 990.M41, a new Tyranid invasion had descended upon the Imperium, and it was named Kraken. Where Hive Fleet Behemoth had fought as a single massive wave that advanced and fought as one, Kraken was actually a series of smaller fleets that moved to attack many worlds simultaneously. Not only did this compound the Imperium's difficulty in opposing the hive fleet, it spread the Shadow in the Warp tenfold. Whole sectors were silenced simultaneously, isolated by the Hive Mind's choking influence. Only months after the onslaught had begun did accounts begin to reach the wider Imperium – grim tales of skies turned black by clouds of poisonous spores and of hulking monsters, ripping and slashing with murderous claws. Stories of billions of creatures swarming across the face of a world, devouring everything in their path. Whole populations had been subdued or wiped out in a single night, and those taken alive had envied the dead.

THE TENDRILS OF KRAKEN

Seen on a galactic scale, Hive Fleet Kraken was attacking across a front that covered thousands of light years, making a cohesive defence impossible to mount. The Imperium was forced to concentrate its forces on the most strategically important worlds, whilst others were evacuated or simply abandoned to their fate.

There were some glimmers of light in the darkness however. Several Space Marine Chapters endeavoured to save those worlds the Imperium had abandoned. Some, such as the Lamenters and the Scythes of the Emperor, paid for their boldness with heavy losses, their once proud Chapters reduced to a few scattered remnants, whilst the Knights of Eternity seemed to have been entirely wiped out. Others carried the battle to the Tyranids in the manner that only Space Marines could, boarding hive ships and blowing them apart from the inside. Yet no matter the effort the Imperium made, the Tyranids were too many, and they drove ever onwards into the galaxy.

ICHAR IV

Fortunately for Mankind, Hive Fleet Kraken did not remain spread out indefinitely, and many of its tendrils converged on Ichar IV, a hive world that some years earlier had been the site of a Genestealer infestation. Thousands of clawed fiends burst from the underhives in support of the invading Tyranids, giving lie to claims that the infestation had been cleansed. Defence perimeters were quickly overrun by the scuttling horrors that had lurked patiently in hiding for so long. In the confusion, ever more Tyranids made planetfall – not merely the Termagants and Gargoyles that had composed the vanguard of Behemoth's assaults, but monstrous Exocrines and Tyrannofexes in scores. Worse still, giant bio-titans now stalked across the surface of the beleaguered planet. The Tyranids had descended on Ichar IV with everything at their disposal.

Despite its woes, Ichar IV was not yet lost. Forewarned by the previous infestation, Marneus Calgar led the Ultramarines to save the Ichar system, inflicting crushing losses on the Tyranid armada in space and in the claustrophobic environs of the towering hive cities. Veterans of the First Tyrannic War made planetfall and scoured Ichar IV's hives in a series of close quarters battles that lasted almost a full year.

In a replay of history, Marneus Calgar faced none other than the Swarmlord – a reincarnation of the same beast that had laid him low on Macragge – during the final battle for Ichar IV. This time, however, it would be Calgar who emerged triumphant, slaying the beast in an epic duel. Without the Swarmlord to counter Calgar's military strategy, the Ultramarines finally cast the Tyranids from the world. Yet victory had come too late to save Ichar IV, which was now little more than a smoking charnel-house of death and destruction – a world sacrificed so that the Imperium might endure. Perhaps worse for the Imperium, the Hive Mind absorbed the Swarmlord's consciousness again, and having learned from its own death, its next reincarnation would surely prove the most dangerous yet encountered.

THE SPLINTER FLEETS

The scattered remnants of the Tyranid attack on Ichar IV fled towards the galactic core, driving well within the defence perimeters drawn against Hive Fleet Kraken. These splinter fleets have, if anything, become an even greater threat as they feed upon unsuspecting and ill-defended worlds far from the major war zones. Running battles with the splinter fleets have continued for many years since Kraken's passage, draining the galaxy's defences against later incursions. It is doubtful if the true extent of the devastation caused by the hive fleet will ever be known.

Splinter fleets can comprise as few as a dozen hive ships, but even a dozen bio-ships are more than capable of overrunning a world and harvesting its biomass to become a yet greater threat. Some have become so large as to be classified as a new, distinct hive fleet. Indeed, Hive Fleet Magalodon is grown from one of Kraken's sundered tendrils, and continues to ravage the Imperium to this day.

Doubtless, the Tyranids have learnt much about the inner galaxy's defences from these splinter fleets. Every battle the Tyranids engage in, won or lost, adds to the Hive Mind's ever-growing understanding of its prey. Was this Hive Fleet Kraken's true goal all along? Who can say? It is perhaps preferable to believe that the Hive Mind had this very eventuality planned from the onset, rather than to entertain the only other possibility: that the Hive Mind has the strategic wit to turn even its defeats into victories elsewhere…

DOOM OF THE ELDAR

At around the same time that one tendril of Hive Fleet Kraken was battling the Imperium on Ichar IV, another was approaching Iyanden, one of the largest and most populous of the Eldar craftworlds. It would be here, amidst eldritch architecture and within wraithbone halls, that the most bloody conflict yet between Eldar and Tyranid would occur.

Though Iyanden's rune-casting Farseers had foreseen echoes of doom upon the future, the first proof of the Tyranid threat was reported by the craftworld's Rangers. A large tendril of Hive Fleet Kraken was headed directly towards Iyanden. It was too vast to outrun and no mere battle line could contain it. Farseer Kelmon, spiritual leader of Iyanden, declared that all would have to fight together if they were to stand a glimmer of hope. The entire craftworld made ready for war, and in a sacred ritual, the Avatar of the Bloody-handed God was awakened.

THE WALKING DEAD

Even with every Eldar on Iyanden armed, the swarm that approached still vastly outnumbered the defenders. With a heavy heart, Kelmon ordered the ghost warriors to be brought forth. In an act considered by many Eldar to be akin to tomb robbing, the spirit stones of Iyanden's ancestors were plucked from their resting places and placed in the wraithbone shells of war-constructs to fight alongside their still-living children. It is a testament to the terrible threat Hive Fleet Kraken posed that it forced the Eldar to commit such a distasteful act. Without the ghost warriors, the Tyranids would have overwhelmed the craftworld, but by waking them from death, Kelmon risked the accumulated wisdom, cultural and racial memories of Iyanden itself.

'Gather the dead for war, let them join our ranks, lest we are forced to join theirs.'

- FARSEER KELMON

THE SHADOW DESCENDS

The first Tyranid swarms attacked Iyanden twenty days later. By then, the craftworld had already been isolated for over a week by the Shadow in the Warp, and a dark malaise hung heavy in every Eldar heart. The Tyranids approached the giant craftworld like a vast shoal of sharks, thousands of bio-ships attacking in unrelenting waves. Iyanden's formidable space fleet destroyed each wave in succession, but the ability of the craftworld's forges to repair and replace lost spacecraft was outstripped by the viciousness of the deep space battles. The Eldar do not fight wars of attrition by choice, and slowly, craft by craft, the Eldar succumbed and the jaws of the Great Devourer closed in on the craftworld. Then, Iyanden was hit by two huge attack waves in quick succession, swarms that dwarfed all the other assaults combined, and the remaining flotilla of Eldar vessels was swept aside. The bloated Tyranid craft blotted out the stars as they descended onto their quarry, vomiting forth armies of hideous creatures into Iyanden's unspoilt havens. A horrific psychic scream resounded around the craftworld's infrastructure as seething hordes of clawed, scuttling aliens were disgorged into its heart.

THE KRAKEN STRIKES

Battles erupted all over Iyanden, the fighting bitter and close ranged, with enemy forces often only separated by the width of a corridor or wall. Eldar Guardians fought bloody battles with vast numbers of Termagants, shuriken fire and fleshborer maggots screeching through the air with equal lethality. Eldar Aspect Warriors and Wraithguard attempted to slice their way through massed swarms of Genestealers and Tyranid Warriors that blocked the arterial corridors like a vile cancer. Above curved halls, Swooping Hawks and Gargoyles fought a deadly aerial dance whilst sleek Eldar jetfighters and bat-winged Crones exchanged roles of hunter and prey at breakneck speeds amidst alabaster spires. Carnifexes wrestled with ancient Wraithlords as Trygons battled towering Wraithknights. Graceful Phantom Titans duelled with grotesque bio-titans, slaying each other over a spore-choked surface. War even raged beyond the material realm as Zoanthropes and Warlocks engaged in mighty psychic duels. The Eldar had no place to hide, no sanctuary the Tyranids could not breach and no warrior or weapon of war that the aliens could not match. Soon, the Eldar's Walking Dead outnumbered the living.

The Eldar warriors sold their lives dearly, exacting a terrible toll in Tyranid corpses, but it was not enough. First the Fortress of Tears fell, then the Shrine of Asuryan was destroyed. Most terrible of all, the deeply spiritual Forests of Silence were ravaged by the Tyranid hordes. It is said that many of the Eldar wept tears of rage and sorrow to see the damage inflicted on their precious forest shrine, realising that they now stood on the brink of extinction.

THE PRODIGAL SON

Word of Iyanden's peril managed to reach Prince Yriel, despite the psychic barriers isolating the craftworld. Though Yriel, exiled long ago from Iyanden, had vowed never to return to the place of his birth, he could not abandon Iyanden in its darkest hour. Tempering his indignation, Yriel and his fleet made best speed to the battle.

Like the burning spear of Khaine, Yriel's forces thrust through Hive Fleet Kraken's blockade and struck deep into the bio-fleet enveloping Iyanden. The renegade prince was an admiral without peer, and upon joining forces with the battered survivors of Iyanden's fleet, the Eldar ripped the heart out of the Tyranid swarm. Yriel prevented any more of Kraken's spawn from reaching the wounded craftworld, whilst simultaneously coordinating counter-strikes on the largest bio-vessels. Kraken launched two further waves but both were destroyed. Bloodied but unbowed, Yriel's forces prepared to sell their lives dearly, for surely another wave would overwhelm them. Minutes passed into hours as the Eldar ships scanned the runes of their scanners awaiting the next assault, but it did not come. The space-borne hive fleet had been defeated.

To Slay a Monster

Under Iyanden's skies, the battle for the craftworld's soul still raged. The Tyranids now turned like cornered rats and hurled themselves at the Eldar with renewed ferocity. A massive Hive Tyrant led the frenzied horde, and neither shuriken nor sword blade could pierce the monster's hide. Wherever the beast attacked, the Eldar were butchered, and across the craftworld, the Tyranids were breaking through, sweeping aside pockets of resistance. The final confrontation was at hand, and victory was within the Hive Mind's grasp.

Amidst the carnage, the Avatar stepped forward. With a growl akin to an erupting volcano, the fiery warrior roared a challenge to the Hive Tyrant, but instead of meeting the iron-clad figure, the monster urged its minions to attack. Not one, but a dozen Carnifexes stampeded towards the flame-wreathed Avatar. Under such an assault, not even the embodiment of the Bloody-handed God could prevail.

With the Avatar lost, the last vestiges of hope ebbed from the Eldar. But, in an act of loyalty that restored Yriel as a hero of his people, the Raider Prince and his forces disembarked from their ships to reinforce Iyanden's survivors. The Tyranids were on the verge of overrunning the Eldar lines when Yriel himself plunged into the fray wielding the cursed Spear of Twilight. This ancient weapon, locked in stasis by Iyanden's seers, was a weapon of such power that it would eventually burn out the life-force of any who wielded it. That Yriel was willing to sacrifice not only his life, but also his immortal soul, was a testament to the drastic measures that had to be taken in order to defeat the Tyranids.

With one fluid motion, Yriel thrust the Spear of Twilight into the Hive Tyrant's gaping maw and out through the back of its chitinous skull. With a howling scream, the Tyrant collapsed and died at Yriel's feet. The last echoes of the monster's death shriek signalled the defeat of the alien horde. With their synaptic conduit severed, the remaining Tyranids ceased to attack as a united wave as they reverted to their base instincts. The scattered alien invaders were systematically hunted and eliminated in a series of vicious one-sided battles. The Tyranid attack on Iyanden was over.

The Cost of Victory

The victory on Iyanden was a hollow one indeed, for though Kraken had been defeated, Iyanden stood in ruins. Four-fifths of Iyanden's population lay dead – a terrible blow for the declining Eldar race. Amongst the slain lay Farseer Kelmon, surrounded by the bodies of a dozen Tyranids whose forms bore the marks of psychic fire. Worse still, all the souls within those spirit stones that had been destroyed by the Tyranids were lost forever; Iyanden would never truly recover. The Eldar had learned a painful lesson and would never again underestimate the threat of the Great Devourer.

Hive Fleet Kraken was now little more than splintered fragments of its former might, yet credit lay neither entirely with the defenders of Iyanden nor the actions of the Ultramarines on Ichar IV. The Eldar and the Imperium had been fighting as unwitting allies – had Kraken not struck Iyanden, the Ultramarines' victory at Ichar IV would have been impossible, and vice versa. Had either Ichar IV or Iyanden fallen, Kraken would have been unstoppable.

THE GORGON

Kraken was not the only hive fleet to plague the galaxy in the wake of Behemoth. Several smaller hive fleets were also sinking their tendrils into the Eastern Fringe, and though they only lightly encroached upon the Imperium's domain, the emergent Tau Empire was not so lucky and soon found itself fighting a war against extinction itself.

Hive Fleet Gorgon, like numerous other Tyranid fleets – including Naga, Chimera and Scarabus – was first thought to be a splintered tendril of Behemoth and not a hive fleet in its own right. Even so, such a distinction is only significant if one forgets that all the Tyranids are ultimately under the direction of one omnipresent sentience. The Hive Mind was testing the defences of the galaxy, probing for a weakness it could exploit and seeking new races to devour. During its search, it had tasted the flesh of the Tau, and now it hungered for more.

The Tau were first alerted to the oncoming hive fleet when several outlying trading planets went mysteriously silent. Soon, a handful of refugee ships escaped to bring word of the alien horrors that had devoured their world. All attempts to establish peaceful contact with the Tyranids met with bloody disaster, and the Tau Fire Caste finally responded by deploying numerous warrior cadres to halt the onslaught.

Despite its relatively small size, Hive Fleet Gorgon posed a dire threat to the unsuspecting Tau. Gorgon still possessed ships enough to overwhelm the Tau space fleets patrolling the borders of their territory, and could unleash untold waves of warrior-organisms to overrun a planet. It was not because of its numbers, though, that Hive Fleet Gorgon would prove so dangerous. More so than any hive fleet encountered before or since, Gorgon possessed an ability to rapidly adapt to new circumstances on a biological level, emerging from every lost battle with a new clutch of organisms perfectly suited to overcome the foes that had defeated their predecessors. It would come to define the very nature of the war against the Tau: adapt or die.

FLESH AGAINST TECHNOLOGY

The Tau chose to draw the line on the forest world of Sha'draig. Other outlying colonies were simply evacuated as the shadow of Gorgon loomed, abandoned so that the Tau could concentrate their forces instead of over-extending themselves across dozens worlds against a numerically superior foe. The Tyranids' first assault on Sha'draig was an overwhelming failure. The Tau patiently waited for the rampaging hordes to close within optimum firing range before felling hundreds with every volley of their pulse rifles. The few large Tyranid organisms that lumbered forwards were systematically felled as Tau battle tanks engaged them at extreme range, sniping the monsters with pin-point ion cannon fire before they ever got within range to use their monstrous claws. A few Tyranids managed to weather the storm of plasma fire, but even these ran headlong into the waiting guns of Tau battlesuits – their bodies blown apart as they were targeted by multiple heavy weapon systems. In their naïvety, the Tau believed their technology was proof against anything the Tyranids could throw at them. Then, another wave of attackers reached the surface of the heavily forested planet.

In response to the powerful pulse rifles of the Tau, Hive Fleet Gorgon restructured its warriors' carapaces to better absorb plasma bursts; the weapons that had proven so murderous were robbed their efficacy. When one shot had slain a Hormagaunt before, two, or even three hits were now required to fell a foe. Worse, towering monsters with giant bio-cannons cradled in fused limbs on their backs now stalked the landscape, hunting Tau tanks at range and blasting apart the Broadside battlesuits that stood sentinel over the beleaguered Tau. In desperation, the Tau fell back under the covering fire of their Kroot allies, whose solid-shot sniper rounds still proved effective. Protected by the cover of the forest, the Kroot were able to keep the Tyranids from getting to grips with them, and their sharp-eyed marksmen slowed the advance of the swarm. But then the Hive Mind unleashed a new wave of creatures; bloated beasts whose dorsal weapons spurted gouts of flame to burn their prey from their wooded sanctuary. Beside them came lithe, snake-like creatures to whom the tangled undergrowth of the forest was no hindrance. They darted between boughs to pounce on the survivors, tearing them apart in an eye-blink.

The Kroot died in their thousands, but their sacrifice bought the Tau enough time to regroup and refit their battlesuits. The Tau began to equip their squads with prototype missile pods and experimental rail rifle weaponry, ballistics that the Tyranids had not before encountered. The war shifted again in the Tau's favour as these new weapons carved furrows into the Tyranids' ranks, and though hard fought and bloody, the second assault was ultimately thwarted. Gorgon proved an implacable foe though, and with its second defeat, the cycle of adaptation began anew.

When the Tyranids next swarmed across Sha'draig's surface, the Hive Mind had spawned gangrel creatures to flit in the midst of its swarm, emitting thick clouds of choking spores that masked the hordes' approach. Plasma and solid shot alike were useless when no target could be seen, and only the missiles of retrofitted Broadside battlesuits worked with any efficiency in the obscuring gloom. Their barrages saturated large areas, and every explosion blasted scores of Tyranids to ash. Soon, however, the ground beneath the Broadsides' feet rumbled before tunnelling Mawlocs burst from below to swallow them whole. The Tau were now too few to make to make an effective stand, and with a heavy heart, they abandoned Sha'draig to the Gorgon and fell back to the sept world of Ke'lshan.

> *'Never have I faced a tide of foes that can alter both strategy and flesh to hasten our downfall. Swift as these beasts adapt, we must be swifter, for if we fail, the Tau Empire will drown in its own blood.'*
> – SHAS'EL VORCAH OF KE'LSHAN

FLIGHT TO KE'LSHAN

Though the Tau fleet was pursued by dozens of bio-ships, only a handful of cadre vessels were boarded and destroyed before the Tau successfully punched through the Tyranid blockade. Unaffected by the Shadow in the Warp, the Tau's ZFR Horizon drives propelled their ships at near light speed through realspace, and arrived safely at Ke'lshan. It took the Tyranids many days to traverse the same span of space, and for the first time in months, the Tau hoped to have a chance to catch their breath and recuperate.

However, upon arriving at Ke'lshan, the Tau found the sept world embroiled in a war against the Imperium of Man. With no time to waste, the Tau fleet fell upon the interlopers, but the Imperium's task force was no mere raiding party. A dozen Imperial Guard regiments of the famed Cadian 18th were already dug in on the planet's surface and determined to reclaim the world in the name of the Emperor. Battle raged for three full days, and all the while, Hive Fleet Gorgon came ever closer.

STRANGE ALLIANCES

It was the Imperium's forces who first detected the Tyranids entering the Ke'lshan system – the mad babblings of the Cadian's Primaris Psyker alerted them to the approaching danger. Faced with a common enemy, the Imperial Guard finally listened to the Tau's calls for a ceasefire and agreed upon an uneasy truce. For one of the few times in recorded history, Imperial Guardsmen and Tau Fire Warriors stood, if not shoulder to shoulder, then at least as brothers in arms, against the Tyranids.

Acting in concert, the Imperial and Tau fleets cut deep into Gorgon's vanguard. Though casualties were heavy, the allies destroyed a majority of the bio-ships, severely reducing the Tyranids' reproductive capacity. The few remaining bio-ships fled the system after deploying their swarms to Ke'lshan's surface, but the Tau pursued, determined to end the threat forever. Meanwhile, on the surface, the allied forces held the line against the Tyranid horde. Three Imperial Guard regiments and two Tau cadres were overrun in the initial onslaught, but the disparate weaponry and tactics employed by the allies prevented the rapid adaptation that had plagued the Tau on Sha'draig. Slowly, the allies' guns drove the swarm back, and during the Battle of Worldspine Ridge, the last Hive Tyrant was slain, leaving the leaderless beasts to be purged with relative ease. Though the alliance with the Cadians ended soon after, Hive Fleet Gorgon was defeated.

> *'Aliens they may be, but I'd rather take my chances with the alien I know. Just make sure they stay between us and those… things.'*
> - CASTELLAN CRASK OF THE CADIAN 18TH

Gorgon would have a lasting legacy for the Tau. Seeing how quickly their technologies had been circumvented, they strived to make new weapon advances. It would be over a century before the Tau were forced to face the Tyranids again, and it remains to be seen whether their latest weapons of war are enough to withstand the Hive Mind's insatiable hunger.

THE SECOND TYRANNIC WAR

897.M41 THE GORGON STRIKES
Hive Fleet Gorgon invades the space of the Tau Empire, thrusting the young race into a deadly battle of survival.

c. 990.M41 THE KRAKEN AWAKES
Hive Fleet Kraken invades the Eastern Fringe and awakens from its long slumber. The Diatan, Salem and Veridian Sectors fall silent as the Shadow of the Warp envelops them.

015990.M41 RAVENS AND KRAKENS
Originally despatched to rescue the remaining population of the planet of Idos, the Raven Guard 4th Company are instead ordered to launch a desperate surgical strike in an attempt to defeat the Tyranid swarm ravaging the world.

156991.M41 THE MARTYRDOM OF SALEM
Confronted with the horror of Hive Fleet Kraken, the monks of the asteroid-monastery of Salem choose to poison themselves and their carefully-tended ecosystem with necrotising rotweed, rather than allow their purified flesh to be consumed by the advancing Tyranids.

225991.M41 THE ICHAR REBELLION
The planet of Ichar IV erupts into rebellion as a faction known as the Brotherhood overthrows the planetary governor. Soon after the fighting breaks out, Inquisitor Agmar, despatched from the Inquisitional fortress on Talasa Prime, leads his battle forces into the planetary capital of Lomas and discovers that at its heart, the rebellion is harbouring a massive Genestealer infestation. Realising the forces under his command are insufficient to combat the threat, Agmar sends an urgent plea for assistance.

332991.M41 CLEANSING OF ICHAR IV
Responding to the Inquisitor's report, the Ultramarines Battle Barge *Octavius* arrives in orbit, carrying two full companies of Space Marines alongside elements of the newly founded, but under strength 1st Company. The Ultramarines lead the attack into the heart of Ichar IV's planetary capital whilst regiments of the Imperial Guard advance in support. The planet is brought back under the heel of the Imperium within three weeks of bitter fighting, and the victors report all trace of the Genestealer infestation has been cleansed from Ichar IV.

689991.M41 THE PRICE OF COURAGE
As part of a century-long crusade of penitence, the Lamenters launch an attack against Hive Fleet Kraken, fighting a series of hopeless battles. Whilst their heroics slow Kraken's advance for a while, the Chapter is brought to the edge of extinction by the horrendous casualty rate inflicted upon it.

750991.M41 MORTREX OVERRUN
The Imperial world of Mortrex is overwhelmed by unrelenting tides of Ripper Swarms.

777991.M41 THE LOSS OF CERES XIV

801991.M41 THE JAWS OF DEFEAT
Kraken sinks its teeth into the mining world of Devlan. The Imperial Guard's carefully prepared defences prove useless against assaults from beneath by tunnelling Tyranid creatures, spearheaded by a monster known to the petrified populace as the Red Terror. Due to the sacrifice of Lamenters Space Marines, the Tyranids are held back long enough to evacuate a few million colonists before Devlan is consumed.

025992.M41 THE DEATH OF SOTHA
Kraken invades Sotha, homeworld of the Scythes of the Emperor, who are overrun by the Tyranids. The Chapter is decimated and the few survivors reluctantly evacuate to Miral Prime to regroup with their off-world forces.

167992.M41 MYSTERY OF ADRI'S HOPE
A refugee ship from Devlan arrives in orbit around Adri's Hope, ominously silent. Those investigating the ship find it to be a blood-drenched abattoir – all aboard mercilessly butchered. Though a breach of quarantine is suspected to have allowed a Tyranid organism to get aboard, nothing is found. Three weeks later, all contact is lost with Adri's Hope.

255992.M41 GOETHE'S LAST STAND
Princeps Goethe of the Imperator Titan *Mettalum Olympus* single-handedly manages to hold back a tendril of Hive Fleet Kraken on the ash-choked plains of Horst Prime. The mighty war engine is finally destroyed when a brood of Hierophant bio-titans pounce on the noble machine like a pack of wild dogs. In the frenzied attack, *Mettalum Olympus'* plasma reactor is breached and the resultant explosion vaporises everything for a mile around, leaving behind a crater that is still visible from orbit – a testament to the sacrifice needed to fight the Tyranids.

451992.M41 THE DEFENCE OF MIRAL
Imperial Guard regiments and the Space Marines of the Scythes of the Emperor Chapter barely hold out against Tyranids on the death world of Miral Prime. Against the onslaught, the Imperium's forces are forced to fall back to a huge rock mesa known locally as the 'Giant's Coffin' to make a defiant last stand. Here, they fight daily against raging hordes of Tyranids. Despite their heroics, the Scythes of the Emperor suffer catastrophic casualties. Faced with the total destruction of their Chapter, the Space Marines reluctantly retreat, leaving Miral Prime to the Kraken.

650992.M41 THE TROPHY HUNTER
Eager to add to his burgeoning collection of skulls, Roghax Bloodhand, warlord of a World Eaters warband of Chaos Space Marines, leads his maniacal host into a headlong attack against a tendril of Hive Fleet Kraken.

849992.M41 TO STRIKE A BLOW
Though too late to save the rain-drenched bastion world of Eorcshia from a splinter fleet of Hive Fleet Kraken, Space Marines of the Deathwatch successfully plant nucleonic charges within the innards of the massive Tyranid bio-ship at the centre of the fleet as it feeds upon the dying planet. Upon the charges' detonation, the entire splinter fleet falls into disorder.

C. 992.M41 THE FALL OF IYANDEN
The Eldar craftworld of Iyanden is subjected to a series of massive Tyranid attacks. The once mighty craftworld musters every warrior at its disposal, living and dead, and is soon embroiled is desperate fighting against wave after wave of Tyranid organisms.

992-993.M41 THE KRAKEN STRIKES
Several tendrils of Hive Fleet Kraken converge on Ichar IV. The full might of the Ultramarines answers Ichar IV's call to arms, and once again, the Hive Mind responds by unleashing the Swarmlord. The experience of Ultramarines' Veterans from the First Tyrannic War proves decisive, and slowly but surely, Kraken's grip on Ichar IV is severed and the Tyranids are scoured from the world.

994.M41 THE SPLINTERS OF KRAKEN
Following the twin defeats at Ichar IV and Iyanden, the scattered remnants of Hive Fleet Kraken flee towards the galactic core, driving well within the defensive lines drawn to combat the Tyranid threat. Though the Kraken as a single entity is defeated, these splinter fleets, varying in size from a few dozen, to a few hundred bio-ships, continue to be a dire threat, preying upon ill-defended worlds to this day.

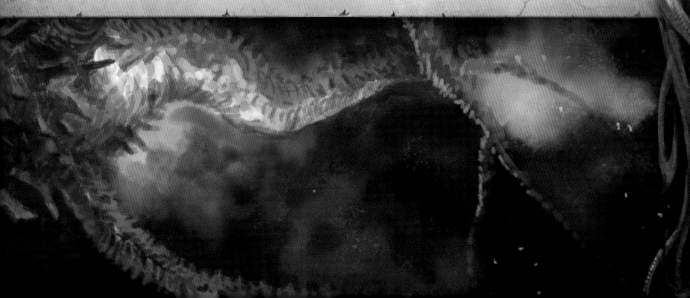

THE LEVIATHAN

At the close of the 41st Millennium, the largest and greatest of the Tyranid hive fleets descended upon the galaxy. The Hive Mind had learnt well the lessons of its earlier invasions, and this new fleet, Leviathan, employed these teachings to the detriment of all other life it encountered.

Once again, it was Inquisitor Kryptman who alerted the High Lords of Terra to the new Tyranid hive fleet, one of terrible size that he named Leviathan. Where the other hive fleets had attacked the Eastern Fringe, striking the galaxy edge-on as they emerged from the intergalactic void, this new hive fleet appeared to have skirted the galactic rim, and was now attacking upwards through the galactic plane.

As with Kraken before, Leviathan did not focus its forces into a single killer blow, but attacked across a broad front. Leviathan's tendrils stretched across the Segmentums Ultima, Tempestus and even Solar. By the time Inquisitor Kryptman could raise the alarm, Leviathan had already advanced far, and the Shadow in the Warp that heralded its coming had orphaned dozens of worlds. The worlds of Valedor and St. Capilene had already been lost, the forge world of Gryphonne IV – home of the mighty War Gryphons Titan Legion – had fallen ominously silent and the agri world of Tarsis Ultra was embroiled in a bloody battle for survival. The morale of the Imperium's forces began to plunge as more worlds were consumed, and with every planet devoured, Leviathan grew stronger.

A DRASTIC MEASURE

With a grim finality, Inquisitor Kryptman ordered that a galactic cordon be established. His plan was that a band of worlds should be evacuated across the path of Leviathan's main advance, with many of them razed to the ground in order to deny the hive fleet any further raw materials for its ships. This would slow its advance long enough for

Battlefleets Solar and Tempestus to muster. Any worlds already under invasion within the bounds of this cordon were to undergo Exterminatus just at the point when the Tyranids descended to feed upon the doomed populace. Kryptman theorised that, using this method, the swarms would expend great resource to claim a world, only to have every living thing upon it reduced to ash by barrages of cyclonic torpedoes and virus bombs. With one stark and callous decision, Kryptman had condemned billions of souls to extermination. To this day, it remains the single largest act of genocide ever inflicted upon the Imperium by its own forces since the Horus Heresy.

Kryptman's decision to abandon hundreds of Imperial worlds in the face of the alien advance was met by howls of outrage by his peers. His butcher's bill was deemed intolerable, and many influential Inquisitors called for Kryptman to be declared Excommunicate Traitoris. When dozens of the cleansed worlds were claimed by the ever-expanding Orks of Octarius, Kryptman's detractors cursed him for a radical, a traitor and a fool. A Carta Extremis was issued, stripping Kryptman of his title and forcing him into exile as a criminal of the worst kind. However, the fact remained that the inexorable advance of Leviathan had slowed to a crawl. Kryptman had bought the Imperium time, that most valuable of commodities, at the expense of a hundred worlds. He had resolved that the many lives he had to sacrifice would not be lost in vain, and had put into action a plan aimed not merely at slowing the advance of Hive Fleet Leviathan, but at dealing it a fatal blow.

KRYPTMAN'S GAMBIT

Despite being cast out of the Inquisition, Kryptman could not abandon his fight against the Hive Mind. As Leviathan continued to spread its tendrils into the Imperium, he took it upon himself to harness the power of the swarm. The former Inquisitor claimed that he could not only defeat Leviathan, but in doing so, he could rid the Imperium of the galaxy's native enemies. Though many of his few remaining allies labelled him a fool, it could not be denied that he understood the Tyranids as no other did. But, as the Imperium would learn, understanding an enemy such as the Tyranids, and controlling it, are two equally impossible things.

Determined to prove his theories right, Kryptman planned to use a tendril of Leviathan to eliminate the Ork Empire of Octarius. The Imperium had long been embroiled in an ever-escalating war against the Orks in this region of space, and despite huge influxes of reinforcements – resources that Kryptman deemed would have been better served fighting the Tyranids – the Orks were dominating the war. Kryptman's gamble was to change the balance of power forever.

Enlisting aid from a squad of Deathwatch Space Marines who still had faith in him, Kryptman captured a live brood of Tyranids and then loaded them onto Perdition's Flame, a space hulk that had emerged from Warp space ahead of the approaching hive fleet. As the Tyranids awoke from stasis, Kryptman destroyed the moon of Gheist, and in doing so, diverted the hulk's trajectory towards the Orks. Within weeks, the Tyranid infestation had spread to dozens of worlds. The Hive Mind had sampled a new feeding ground, and in response, a tendril of Leviathan veered towards Octarius. At first, it appeared that Kryptman's gamble had succeeded.

As Tyranids and Orks fought an endless war across the sector, the Imperium was content to let the alien forces wipe each other out. However, both Orks and Tyranids are races that thrive on war. Greenskins flocked to join the fight from light years around, and every Ork devoured provided yet more biomass to feed the growing Tyranid swarm. It soon became apparent that Kryptman had only delayed the inevitable, for whichever aliens emerged from the conflict as victors would do so stronger than ever before.

WAR IN OCTARIUS

Kryptman had lured Hive Fleet Leviathan into the Ork-held Octarius Sector in the hope that the two alien species would annihilate each other. Where another race would have been terrified at the approaching swarm, the Orks were jubilant – after all, they live for a good fight. Only time would tell if, in the Tyranids, the Orks might finally have met their match.

The first world of the Octarius Sector to feel Leviathan's hunger was Orrok. Above the Orks' settlements, thunder rumbled and the skies turned from blue to black as bio-ships entered orbit. Weirdboy psykers began to gibber in fear – something was clawing at the backs of their brains, something with an infinite hunger focused upon the Orks like the eye of a starving predator. Then the storm broke.

THE DEMISE OF ORROK

Millions of warrior-organisms swarmed across Orrok. To the Ork mind, the best form of defence is to beat the enemy to death, so it was not long before a tide of greenskins crashed headlong into the oncoming Tyranid swarm. Thousands of aliens of both races died in a matter of seconds as blades and fangs sank home. All semblance of strategy was lost, replaced by blind fury, but the Orks' enthusiasm for war could not defeat the Tyranids' overwhelming numbers. By nightfall, every single greenskin on Orrok was dead, their bodies reconstituted and channelled back to the orbiting bio-ships to create yet more Tyranids. Death had come to the Octarius Sector.

THE WAAAGH! WITHOUT END

Dozens of worlds were soon crawling with Tyranids, and every time the skies darkened, the Orks planetside would give a great roar of delight, slapping each other on the backs and grinning fiercely as for once, the fight came to them. The greatest battle centred on the planet of Octaria itself, heart of the Ork empire. Billions of Orks and Tyranids clashed over Octaria's mountainous terrain, both forces sending a near constant stream of reinforcements into a grinding war of attrition. The ground underfoot turned into a crimson mulch of spilt blood and alien ichor. It was total, unremitting, endless violence, and the Orks loved it.

The battle for Octaria continued to escalate, and neither side had a shortage of numbers. Orks streamed in from distant sectors to join the fight of the century, and Tyranid bio-ships produced fresh waves of warriors as quickly as they could assimilate biomass. So it was that, as the war on Octaria raged, Leviathan was forced to seek out nearby prey worlds whose biomass could be fed into the meatgrinder.

THE GHORALA SWARM

In their search, a handful of Leviathan's scout ships happened across the world of Ghorala, a planet rich in biomass and base to Skarfang, Pirate-Warboss of the dreaded Skar Fleet. This mighty, if ramshackle, armada fell upon the bio-ships before they could react. The Tyranid fleet was all but destroyed under Skarfang's guns. However, amidst the carnage, a single bio-ship broke through the Ork blockade, pouncing on the planet as a starving man might snatch at a scrap of bread. Alien blood and viscera spilt into the vacuum of space, but in its death throes the bio-ship delivered several broods of Tyranids to the world's surface. Skarfang grew glum as he realised the battle was over, and he resolved to join the fight on Octaria, as the few Tyranids that had made planetfall were soon stomped out.

THE SWARM SURVIVES

For the first time since the Tyranids had invaded the Octarius Sector, they found themselves embroiled in a war where they were vastly outnumbered by their prey. Skarfang's horde was mighty, and somehow, the Tyranids sensed that a war of attrition would only end in their demise. In response, the Ghorala swarm adapted in order to survive. At first, the Tyranids stalked and preyed upon isolated Ork patrols, but the greenskins soon took to scouring the landscape in mobs too large for the fledgling swarm to face. Forced to abandon their guerrilla war, the Tyranids adopted an altogether more cunning strategy and engaged the Orks in the open. The Tyranids attacked without thought of survival, every action aimed at maximising the carnage. Despite the Tyranids' frenzied attacks, the Orks' superior numbers gave them the advantage in these brutal skirmishes. Whenever the Tyranids were on the verge of being overrun, they would, in eerie unison, switch from

hyperactive slaughter to hasty retreat. The Tyranids lurked in nearby caverns or else burrowed beneath the soil to shelter from pursuant search parties. In the dead of night, synapse creatures re-mustered the scattered swarms to the corpse-choked battlefield. There, the Tyranids fed on Ork cadavers and Tyranid carcasses alike, before returning to digestion pools secreted in the planet's rocky mesas. Slowly but surely, the Tyranids' numbers started to grow.

SKARFANG'S FURY

As the Tyranid forces swelled, they changed their methodology yet again, growing more aggressive and seeking out ever larger concentrations of Orks. Though the Tyranids' reward for their victories was ever-increasing masses of bio-resources, the increased violence soon attracted the bored Skarfang to the surface to join the fray. Wherever Skarfang's guttural war-cries were heard, the Orks attacked with renewed vigour. Even when the Tyranids looked to be on the cusp of victory, the Warboss was able to turn the tide, bellowing blood-curdling threats that encouraged his Boyz to get stuck back in. The Tyranids were being pushed back by the resurgent Ork front; slowly the swarm was being trampled to death. Despite the Tyranids' earlier success, there was little chance that they could face a united Ork force of such magnitude and survive. Whilst Skarfang lived, the Ghorala swarm was doomed.

> *'Dis ain't no stinkin' scrap against puny gits dat run and hide behind walls when the killing starts, dis is proper fightin'.'*
> - PIRATE-WARBOSS SKARFANG

DIVIDE AND CONSUME

In response, the Tyranids created Lictors with the express purpose of eliminating the Ork Warboss. Within days, the Lictors had tracked their eminent quarry, but Skarfang's packs of Squig-hounds foiled all attempts to get close enough to assassinate their target. Although eternally patient, lying in wait for a chance to strike down their target was a luxury the starving swarm could ill afford. So instead, they created an opportunity.

Following pheromone trails, a scuttling tide of Hormagaunts was thrown at the Ork lines. As the Orks roused to man their rusty barricades, Tyranid Warriors willed the scuttling masses to withdraw. Skarfang's frustration rose to infuriation as the Tyranids repeated these feints, approaching from different directions to within an arm's length, then withdrawing before the Orks could retaliate. On the tenth such retreat, Skarfang's temper could take no more. With a roar, the Warboss ordered his mobs to pursue the retreating swarms. Soon, black smoke was belching skywards as Battlewagons and Trukks rumbled after the swarm. The Tyranids had succeeded in goading the Warboss, separating him from the bulk of his forces and luring him into an ambush.

The Tyranids had spawned broods of Venomthropes to blanket the greenskins in a thick, toxic fog. As the Orks pursued their quarry, they rode headlong into the sudden, blinding mist. The entire convoy ground to a halt as vehicles skidded into rocky outcrops or else lost control and ploughed into each other. Coughing and hacking, those Orks that hadn't choked on their own blood pulled themselves from the wreckage. Skarfang himself stumbled across the battlefield and happened across the tentacled beasts responsible for creating the noxious cloud. As he vented his anger on the venomous creatures, the fog receded and the eviscerated corpses of Orks surrounded the Warboss. Lictors had stalked through the blinding cloud and dispatched the unwary greenskins one at a time until only Skarfang remained. The Lictors closed on their true quarry, surrounding the Warboss in deathly silence. Revving his chainblade into life, Skarfang charged the nearest with a roar of defiance. He managed two steps before a dozen mantis-like claws pierced his form and tore him asunder.

With Skarfang dead, it was not long before vying Ork bosses started fighting amongst themselves to fill the power vacuum. The Orks were soon divided, and the disparate bands became easy prey to the united Tyranid swarm. Each was isolated and destroyed in quick succession, and within days, the Orks on Ghorala had been slaughtered like cattle. The Tyranids gorged themselves on their flesh.

THE SWARM REBORN

From the digested remains of Ghorala, the swarm created new bio-ships and set forth to rejoin the hive fleet at Octaria, the biomass it had consumed destined to fuel the next phase of planetary invasion. Though the war for Octaria rages still, one thing is already clear: despite the machinations of Kryptman and the ferocity of the Orks, Leviathan shows no signs of stopping. The Tyranids are not only surviving the Octarian War, they are thriving in it.

THE FALL OF SHADOWBRINK

As Hive Fleet Leviathan drifted into the dead-zone left by Kryptman's evacuations, the Tyranids found world after world reduced to empty shells. Yet one planet, the cathedral world of Shadowbrink, still stood defiant. As the Hive Mind stretched out its mighty tendrils to claim Shadowbrink for its own, it could not know the horrors its hunger was about to unleash.

When the order to evacuate reached Shadowbrink's rulers, they stood paralysed with indecision. Their orders from Segmentum Command were clear, and there could be little doubt that Shadowbrink faced the onrushing fury of a sizeable tendril of Hive Fleet Leviathan. Yet beneath its swooping gothic spires and macromausolea, Shadowbrink's capital city of Rossov concealed a terrible secret. In a vast sepulchre, buried deep beneath the city's streets, there lurked a ring of obscene archeotech dating back to the Dark Age of Technology. Upon its discovery by Inquisitorial acolytes, some three decades earlier, the foul relic had been christened the Maelstrom Cradle. Emitting a steadily strengthening Warp-signature and fluctuating patterns of empyric overbleed, this evil device had resisted all efforts at destruction. Thus, a permanent garrison of Grey Knights had been assigned to stand sentry over it, performing daily rituals of warding while their Librarians worked to permanently seal the potential daemonic rift. With the onset of Hive Fleet Leviathan, it appeared the Grey Knights had run out of time, yet their leader – Brother-Librarian Cadulon – could not permit evacuation while there was a chance the rift might burst asunder. Were Daemons allowed to spill through onto Shadowbrink, there was a very real chance that the Imperium would be faced with a major daemonic incursion on top of the woes of attempting to battle Hive Fleet Leviathan. This was a threat that Imperial forces could ill afford. Employing his authority, Cadulon instructed Shadowbrink's Governor to refuse the order to evacuate his people, instead commanding that the defences be readied to repulse the approaching Tyranids.

TO THE LAST MAN…

Shadowbrink was an important world, its populous cities replete with ancient and priceless relics. As such, it did not stand helpless before the Leviathan. Alongside the planet's civil defence forces and frateris militia were two full regiments of Cadian infantry and another of Vostroyan armour, not to mention the small but deadly force of Grey Knights led by Cadulon himself. In orbit, Shadowbrink was watched over by three mighty orbital defence platforms bristling with lance and torpedo batteries, and an attendant squadron of no less than six Cobra Class Imperial Destroyers. Yet as the planet's deep-space scanners began to fill with an ever-increasing blizzard of blood-red contact icons, it became apparent that such a force would not be anything like enough to weather the oncoming storm.

To their credit, Shadowbrink's orbital defences survived over three hours before being overwhelmed. Yet soon enough, the Cobras and orbital platforms were reduced to empty hulks, their frantic defenders butchered by vast waves of Crones, Harpies, and spore-borne Tyranid war-beasts. As the skies darkened above Shadowbrink and the mind-curdling Shadow in the Warp cocooned it in horror, billions of Tyranid organisms descended upon the stricken planet. Tides of mindless organisms overran the Imperial trench-lines, the Hive Mind spending the lives of its minions at a merciless rate to ensure the prey world's swift demise. Valiant Guardsmen stood shoulder to shoulder until the last, yet none could withstand the onslaught. All across Shadowbrink, in every major settlement and city, the same scene was repeated as outmatched defenders vanished screaming beneath heaving tides of claws and fangs.

At the last, as the numberless Tyranid hordes spilled into the vault holding the Maelstrom Cradle, Cadulon and his handful of followers strode to meet them. A pair of Nemesis Dreadknights led the charge, vast blades hewing xenos monsters apart in droves, yet even these noble champions could not survive forever against the swarm. One by one, Cadulon's brethren fell, their defiant war cries replaced by a sickening crunching as the Grey Knights' corpses were hurriedly devoured. Yet as the Tyranids swept from the vault to begin their consumption of the slaughtered world, they were oblivious to the sulphurous runes beginning to smoulder on the Maelstrom Cradle's flanks.

FROM THE MAELSTROM'S HEART

Mere hours after Cadulon's hopeless charge, the fate that the Grey Knights had striven to avoid came to pass. Gorged on the spilled souls of millions of dead humans, the Maelstrom Cradle roared violently to life. Crackling corposant danced around the vault and the bilious, migraine-hued light of nightmares blazed from the heart of the Maelstrom Cradle. Amid cacophonous gibbering and inhuman shrieks of anticipation, daemonic legions boiled from the widening rift. Coalescing from thin air like hideous, animate tumours, a vast tide of Warp-fiends spilled up through the tunnels and catacombs below Rossov city to erupt onto its corpse-choked streets. Wading through the tide of lesser Daemons came a mighty warlord of each Chaos God. The Bloodthirster, Hak'Vasha, roared Khorne's praises as the Great Unclean One Shub'Luth'Gug lumbered forth alongside him, chuckling in a wet and rumbling baritone. Slipping more cautiously through the rift, the Lord of Change K'rix'xi'kra watched keenly as its old rival – the Keeper of Secrets Lesh'Jae'Thi'Hah – loped ahead in search of adoring victims to slay. This cabal of mighty Daemons – known in Imperial Daemon-lore as the Quadrifold Abominatum – had brought low a myriad of worlds during the Imperium's ten thousand years, and had set their sights upon Shadowbrink as their latest twisted conquest. Yet it took only moments for the lords of the incursion to sense that something was very much amiss.

THE WRATH OF THE WARP

As the daemonic horde ran amok through Rossov, their momentum faltered. Where they had expected cowering mortals upon which to feast, they found only a charnel house of piled corpses that writhed with gnawing Rippers. The buildings were tumbled ruins, and the city was smothered by a blanket of muffling psionic static that caused the Daemons to flicker and fade. Casting their otherworldly perceptions across Shadowbrink, the Daemon lords' confusion turned to outrage at the seething tide of aliens that choked the surface and skies. These creatures had no souls to corrupt, manipulate or twist. They could no more be led into damnation than a lump of rock. Yet the Tyranids' mere presence was a challenge that the Daemons could not ignore, and if the daemonic legions must first exterminate these proliferate vermin before turning their attentions to the Imperium, then so be it. With thousands more daemonic foot-soldiers pouring from the Maelstrom Cradle every minute, the Abominatum prepared to unleash their minions upon the Tyranid swarms and scour them from the face of Shadowbrink. Warp energy flared forth in roaring waves, causing the very stones of Rossov and the flesh of its fallen to writhe. As reality convulsed, an insane citadel rose into being, a fitting seat of power from which the Abominatum would prosecute their war of extermination.

SLAUGHTER ON THE PLAINS

Until this point, the Hive Mind had utterly ignored the emergent Daemon forces. While it recognised that a psychic disturbance of some magnitude was occurring on the planet's northern landmass, the gestalt consciousness of the Tyranid swarm detected neither fresh biomass nor a direct challenge from this strange phenomena, and deemed it irrelevant. However, this bizarre instinctive standoff was not to last, for the minions of the Dark Gods revel in the destruction they can wreak in the material realm. Millions of Daemons poured from the gates of the impossible fortress that rose from the grave of Rossov. Thundering Bloodcrushers and trilling Fiends crashed into grazing swarms of Tyranid organisms, hacking left and right with gleeful abandon. Plaguebearers and Nurglings spilled across Shadowbrink's northern plains in a tide of shambling foulness, their mere touch poisoning the biosphere upon which the Hive Mind fed. Clanking, bellowing Soul Grinders tore down towering spore chimneys, trampling them with petulant ferocity while Pink Horrors capered amid the digestion pools, transmuting the rich vitriolic acids within to kaleidoscopic flame. The Hive Mind responded like a wounded animal, its feeder organisms recoiling frantically from this strange new foe as clouds of spores spat from the bellies of orbiting bio-ships. Yet even the sky above Rossov was now rebelling at the otherwordly incursion, shuddering between the grim reality of the blotted stars and a roiling vista of racing, bloodshot storm clouds. As the spores plunged through this twisted stormscape, they were ravaged by daemonic energies, exploding into sparkling rains of cinder and ash. Those that made planetfall struck as ossified orbs that shattered on impact, or burst open to spill tides of rank, malformed foulness that mewled and twitched even as they writhed with corpulent maggots.

The sodden agri-plains around Rossov had been transformed by the Tyranids into a twisted nightmare of fleshy tendrils and sizzling sludge. Now, thundering across this tortured landscape, came a vast herd of Tyranid beasts. Hormagaunts, Termagants and Raveners raced ahead of hulking Carnifexes and Tyranid Warriors. Yet the Tyranid land-offensive met with little more success than had their attack from orbit. As the Tyranids closed upon the Daemons' vanguard, the roiling clouds above split open with a scream like a billion tortured souls, and a rain of bile and blood began to fall. Greasy, daemonic ichor turned the mud of the plains to dilute muck that bogged down the Tyranid forces. Flaming Daemon chariots swooped down upon their struggling foes. As the Tyranids slithered amid the puddles and pus they were scoured by magical flames, hundreds of warrior organisms dying in minutes as their flesh bubbled and vaporized. Flocks of shrieking Furies harried the Tyranids from above, dodging and weaving around the gobbets of hissing bio-acid. As the Tyranids continued to press forwards in their millions, clambering over their own half-submerged dead amid the worsening deluge, the thrum of foetid wings filled the air. A great swarm of Plague Drones descended upon the struggling Tyranids, stabbing and slashing to tear heads from shoulders and shatter chitinous carapaces. Daemonettes danced feather-light across the surface of the mire, weaving aside from frantically slashing talons as they gloried in the abundance of writhing, desperate flesh. A lumbering wave of Haruspexes pressed into the mayhem. Their serrated gullets spat forth to snare Daemons and drag them whole into their maws, only to find the strange flesh rebelling within them, bursting the biohorrors' guts open like rotten seed pods.

THE TIDE TURNS

Even as the masters of the daemonic horde strode forward to join the battle, so the Hive Mind was adapting. Now it viewed the rampant Daemons not as prey, but as rival predators endangering the food source. The Tyranids' efforts were redoubled, and they raced to devour Shadowbrink's biomass before it could be spoiled. As vast tides of Rippers scoured the planet's southern and equatorial continents, the Hive Mind threw every war beast it had against the Warpspawn. This new enemy could reshape the rules of reality and were as deadly at close quarters as the Tyranids themselves. Thus, the Hive Mind despatched swarms of Exocrines and Biovores to form a vast cordon that ringed the emergent Daemonic forces. As one, this apocalyptic living artillery battery tensed and unleashed a barrage of unimaginable scale on the foe. Crackling orbs of bioplasmic energy rained down upon the Daemons, annihilating them in their thousands. Clouds of Spore Mines drifted through the downpour, detonating in clouds of whizzing bone shrapnel.

> 'This world, this galaxy, all of it is ours to twist and corrupt as we will! Such elaborate artistry have we planned for the flesh and souls that you would, in your ignorance, gobble like mindless beasts. We shall cast you back into the outer dark from whence you came, for this reality is the plaything of the children of the Eye, and you have no place in it!'
> - LESH'JAE'THI'HAH, KEEPER OF SECRETS

The daemonic offensive faltered and the Hive Mind pushed scores of Tervigons to the fore. For hour after hour, waves of fresh Termagants spilled from the bloated bodies of their brood-mothers, hunkering down amid the churned muck of Shadowbrink's plains to rain volley after volley of fleshborer beetles upon the faltering Daemons. Shub'Luth'Gug, Great Unclean One of Nurgle, attempted to break the deadlock and push through the Tyranid cordon. Yet even as the ponderous mountain of filth marshalled his psychic energies, they were smothered by the Shadow in the Warp. Moments later, the huge Daemon was blown apart in a catastrophic deluge of foul viscera as broods of hovering Zoanthropes, striking with uncanny coordination, pierced his bloated hide with a barrage of searing psychic blasts.

With one of their number fallen, the remaining lords of the Abominatum realised the nature of the battle had changed. The Hive Mind was leeching their energies, severing the Daemons from the sustaining powers of the Empyrean. No real blood flowed for Khorne, just worthless alien ichor. As each rancid disease was unleashed by the children of Nurgle, so the next brood of Tyranids had grown resistant to it. Without the fear or devotion of true mortals to sustain them, the Daemons were foundering fast.

As hours turned to days without relief from the successive waves of Tyranids, the daemonic numbers thinned as they lost their grip upon reality. The Lord of Change, K'rix'xi'kra, blasted its way back to the shattered heart of what was left of Rossov city, and made good its escape through the flickering Maelstrom Cradle. The remaining two Greater Daemons, Hak'Vasha and Lesh'Jae'Thi'Hah, led a final, mad charge to break the Tyranid lines, turning all of their boundless ire upon the creatures before them.

Yet the Hive Mind, having absorbed its foes' strategies, predicted their attack. Even as the Bloodthirster and Keeper of Secrets pounded forwards at the head of ten thousand minions, a mighty swarm of Tyrannofexes and Trygons surged to meet them. As one bio-round after another slammed into their corrupt flesh, the daemonic lines collapsed. With sudden, abrupt fury, the Maelstrom Cradle imploded in upon itself, the daemonic citadel collapsing with a thunderous, sucking roar. The Bloodthirster, Hak'Vasha, was the last Daemon dragged back into the Warp – its unholy form was still wrestling furiously with three monstrous Trygons as it was wrenched from the mortal plane. The creature's bellows of fury faded slowly into silence. On Shadowbrink the Hive Mind had won a mighty victory against the legions of Chaos. Yet even as the Tyranids returned their attentions to devouring the ruined world, in the twisted realm of the Warp, malevolent intelligences smouldered with fury and plotted their revenge.

'The more I learn about these aliens, the more I come to understand what drives them, the more I hate them. I hate them for what they are and for what they may one day become. I hate them not because they hate us, but because they are incapable of good, honest, human hatred.'

- Inquisitor Agmar

Hive Fleet Moloch
Hive Fleet Jormungandr
HALO STARS
GHOUL STARS
THE EYE OF TERROR
ULTIMA SEGMENTUM
DACIA
SHADRAC
THE MAELSTROM
HOLY TERRA
Hive Fleet Kraken
SEGMENTUM SOLAR
OBLITERAX
CRUSADE OF WRATH
TELLERAN
OCTARIA
GHEIST
STORMVALD
NEW HOPE
POSUL
NEWFOUND
TAU EMPIRE
CARPATHIA
ICHAR IV
Hive Fleet Gorgon
SEGMENTUM TEMPESTUS
FORGEFANE
MACRAGGE
TARSIS ULTRA
NIHILAS
PRANDIUM
JORN V
ST. CASPALEN
GRYPHONNE IV
RIGANT
TIRATHAIN
Hive Fleet Behemoth
SONDHEIM V
ULIK SECTOR
TESLA PRIME
VEILED REGION
GALACTIC PLANE
Hive Fleet Leviathan
Hive Fleet Hydra
Hive Fleet Leviathan

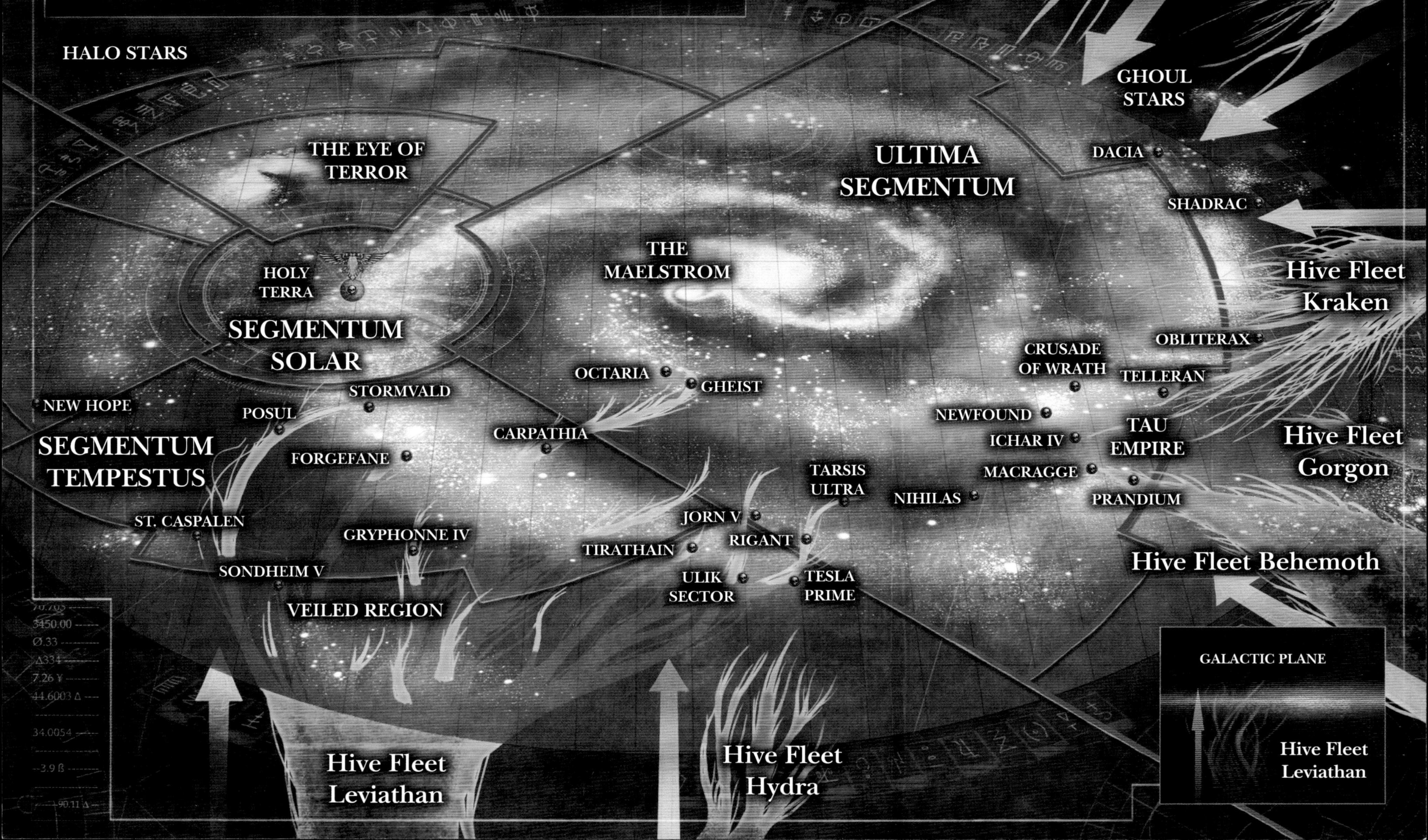

The Third Tyrannic War

c. 997.M41 The Coils of Pythos
The Red Talons Space Marines hold the fortress world of Orask on the edge of the Ghoul Stars from an invading splinter of Hive Fleet Pythos.

138997.M41 The Leviathan Arises
Hive Fleet Leviathan strikes at the underbelly of the Imperium, sinking its tendrils into Segmentums Tempestus, Ultima and Solar.

250997.M41 Slaughter of St. Caspalen
Blood stains the cloisters as Leviathan invades the shrine world of St. Caspalen. The world's leaders are slain and terrorised by a Tyranid assassin and, riven with panic, the planet's defence forces are easy prey. The only true resistance comes from a force of Sisters of Battle who hold out bravely for weeks, but even they are overwhelmed when Deathleaper lures Trygons to excavate beneath their holy bastion and swarms of Hormagaunts use the tunnels in their wake to flood the fortification. The loss of St. Caspalen is a blow to the Imperium, and a manifest warning that faith alone is no defence against the Tyranids.

302997.M41 The Swarmlord Returns
Leviathan's swiftest victories occur along a spine of worlds in the Hodur Sector. In the span of a single year, the Swarmlord oversees the absorption of dozens of worlds, including Talon – homeworld of the Storm Falcons Space Marines Chapter.

360997.M41 The Folly of Pride
The supposedly impenetrable Iron Warriors fortress world of Forgefane falls to the Tyranids in less than a week.

400997.M41 Battle of Bloodstar
Battlefleet Ultima concludes a disastrous campaign against Leviathan when it is ambushed and entrammelled by two separate Tyranid fleets in the Bloodstar Sector and the celebrated flagship, *Imperial Glory*, is destroyed.

498997.M41 A World Abandoned
The Adeptus Mechanicus abandon the world of Tesla Prime, choosing to use its military forces to bolster Gryphonne IV, one of the principal forge worlds in the galaxy, in preparation for a defiant stand against Hive Fleet Leviathan.

509997.M41 Defence of Tarsis Ultra
Leviathan invades Tarsis Ultra as the first snows of winter begin to fall. Despite the presence of the Ultramarines and the Mortifactors, the tide of battle turns against the armies of the Imperium due to the Tyranids' sheer numbers. Tarsis Ultra is saved not by force of arms alone, but through a biological plague created by Magos Locard and delivered into the very heart of the hive fleet by Uriel Ventris of the Ultramarines 4th Company. All attempts to replicate a similar contagion have thus far resulted in failure.

899997.M41 Mass Exterminatus
Inquisitor Kryptman orders the destruction of hundreds of worlds to create a cordon to slow the advance of Hive Fleet Leviathan.

066998.M41 The Battle for Gryphonne IV
Skies darken with bio-ships over the forge world of Gryphonne IV, home of the War Gryphons Titan Legion. Combined with the planet's Skitarii legions and the military forces of Tesla Prime, the Adeptus Mechanicus prepare for war.

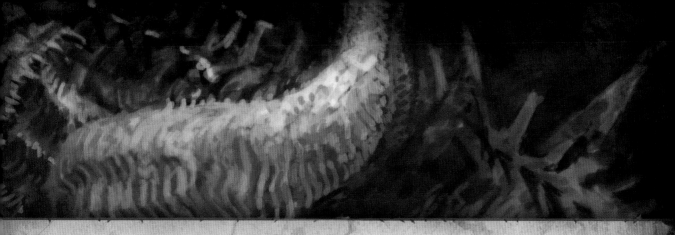

When Tyranid warrior-organisms reach the planet's surface, a battle of truly epic scale unfolds. The landscapes of metal and girder run black with ichor as heavy weaponry takes a fearsome toll on the invaders. Within an hour, the ground shakes to the tread of Titans, emerging from their cathedral hangars to engage the huge monstrosities stalking through the manufactorum.

However, for every bio-titan that falls to the fury of the Mechanicus' guns, one of the Imperium's giant war machines is torn apart by enormous bladed claws, volleys of bio-cannon fire and gouts of hissing pyro-acid. The ground reverberates to the tread of duelling giants for days on end, the Adeptus Mechanicus and the swarms of the Hive Mind both refusing to give.

Despite the resolve of the Tech-Priests and the toll their machines reap on the Tyranids, the Tyranid invasion gathers pace. Slowly but surely, the defenders of Gryphonne IV are overwhelmed by the unending swarm, and even the mighty Titans of the War Gryphons are brought crashing down.

Within days, the world is scoured. Though the loss of Gryphonne IV is a calamity of unprecedented scale for the Imperium, the Tyranids are uncaring of their victory and Hive Fleet Leviathan simply moves on in search of fresh feeding grounds.

755998.M41 A Bloody Harvest
A lone bio-ship launches an invasion against the planet Stormvald. The Phoenix Lord Maugan Ra stands alone against the swarm, and triumphs.

854998.M41 The Fall of Shadowbrink
Hive Fleet Leviathan descends upon Shadowbrink, annihilating all the prey world's defenders and unwittingly triggering a daemonic incursion.

932998.M41 Stuck in the Craw
Hive Fleet Leviathan fights the Imperial Guard regiments of Catachan on the death world of Jorn V. Though outnumbered, the Catachan Jungle Fighters prove stubbornly resourceful and slow the Tyranids' advance long enough for additional Imperial Guard and Space Marine reinforcements to arrive planetside and strike a vital blow against the hive fleet.

200999.M41 Kryptman's Gambit
Kryptman undertakes a dangerous mission on the labyrinth world of Carpathia. Leading several specially equipped Deathwatch teams into the heart of the planet's caverns, Kryptman succeeds in capturing a live Genestealer brood in a stasis field, though many of the Space Marines die in the attempt.

550999.M41 The Crusader Thwarted
High Marshal Helbrecht of the Black Templars, in pursuit of the Ork Warlord Ghazghkull Thraka, leads a fleet forged from fifteen Space Marine Chapters against a splinter tendril of Hive Fleet Leviathan which is barring his path. Despite employing every strategy and ploy at his disposal, Helbrecht's fleet is continually forced to fall back before the Tyranid advance. His mounting ire matches the rising numbers of the Space Marines lost to the Leviathan.

650999.M41 Perdition's Flame
Kryptman and his allies board the space hulk *Perdition's Flame* and lodge his clutch of captured Genestealers aboard. Kryptman then orders the destruction of the moon of Gheist, diverting the space hulk's path into the system-wide Ork empire of Octarius.

718999.M41 The Octarian War

990999.M41 The Burnings
Eldar from Biel-Tan and Saim-Hann Craftworlds utterly devastate a swathe of Imperial and Ork-held worlds surrounding the war-torn Octarius Sector, with the intent of creating a band of dead worlds that will halt the spread of Hive Fleet Leviathan.

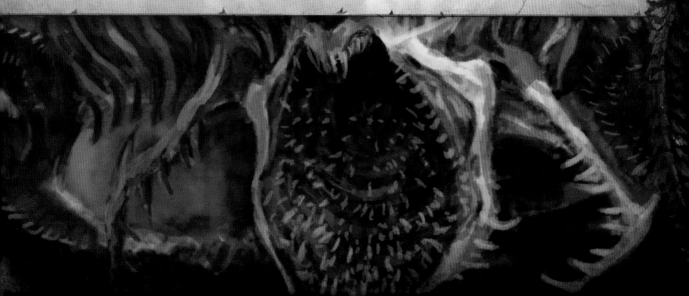

GALACTIC FEEDING GROUNDS

As Hive Fleet Leviathan continues to coil its tendrils around the galaxy, entire worlds are being scoured of life, and hundreds more are embroiled in a desperate fight for survival. So far, all attempts to slay Leviathan have resulted in death and failure, and the Hive Mind's inexorable advance shows no signs of stopping.

The Great Devourer has sunk its tendrils deep into the galaxy, and thus far, it has shown only the first hints of its true strength. Leviathan's encroachment could not have happened at a worse time for the Imperium, for the Imperial Tarot have predicted a time of darkness for the galaxy, unmatched since the bleakest hours of the Horus Heresy. All portents indicate that the arch-traitor Abaddon the Despoiler is on the verge of launching his 13th Black Crusade, and the Imperium can ill afford to leave its back unguarded against a foe as powerful as Hive Fleet Leviathan as it turns to face the imminent Chaos onslaught.

The Adeptus Terra has been sufficiently shaken by the constant flow of Tyranid invasion reports to convene the High Lords of Terra. Their rapid and succinct conclusion is that the inroads Leviathan has made into the Imperium must be stopped at all costs; the Tyranid race must, if possible, be utterly exterminated. The military juggernaut of the Imperium's armed forces are slowly being marshalled to face the Tyranid threat – the Imperium will not submit to the Great Devourer without a fight.

EVER EMERGING THREATS

Unfortunately for the Imperium and the other races of the galaxy, it is not only Leviathan that is assailing the galaxy. New hive fleets are even now beginning to emerge from their cold sleep through the intergalactic void. Hive Fleet Medusa, mistakenly thought by the Imperium to be another tendril of Leviathan, was last recorded feasting upon the ice-world of Shadrac. Hive Fleet Moloch's inexorable advance from the galactic north is also gathering momentum as it devoured the Kiltor Sector and now the Tarellian civilisation. Perhaps most worrying of all are Hive Fleets Scylla and Charybdis carving parallel paths up through the Segmentum Pacificus and Solar, the closest known Tyranid threat to Holy Terra. Though the Imperium might have a little time left to prepare its defences against these twin threats, Saim-Hann Craftworld is caught in the jaws of these two hive fleets, and cannot easily navigate a path to avoid one without risking falling into the clutches of the other.

None know for sure how many other hive fleets still lie dormant within the void, slowly approaching our galaxy to wake and feed. Nor are the threats of previous Tyranid invasions truly over. The splintered fleets of Hive Fleet Kraken are regaining their strength as they feast on a bounty of worlds ill-prepared to defend themselves whilst the galaxy looks to supposedly greater threats. Long dormant remnants of Hive Fleet Jormungandr stir to life, bringing several Imperial worlds to the brink of destruction. Rumours even abound that remnants of Hive Fleet Behemoth, thought slain over two centuries ago, continue to ravage populations and settlements within Ultima Segmentum, with scattered reports of Tyranid attacks on worlds from Calth to Macragge and beyond. With so many threats emerging from unseen quarters, many worlds are holding back from reinforcing the fight against Hive Fleet Leviathan, choosing to preserve their forces for wars closer to home.

HIVE FLEET HYDRA

Hive Fleet Hydra is only now beginning to stir from its aeons-long hibernation. It was the Dark Eldar of the Poisoned Fang Kabal who first encountered this still dormant hive fleet on the very extremes of the eastern spiral arm. Instead of destroying the vulnerable hive fleet, the Dark Eldar boarded the largest bio-vessels, intent on bringing new specimens back to their Kabal's Haemonculi. However, the Dark Eldar were unprepared for the rate at which the bio-ships awoke, and every pirate that set foot inside one of the living ship was killed, butchered by a frenzied tide of Tyranids spawned to protect the ship. The remaining Dark Eldar fleet attempted to escape, but for every drone ship they destroyed, two more took its place. Prematurely awakened from its slumber, Hive Fleet Hydra has accelerated its advance into the galaxy to slake its hunger.

A GLIMMER OF HOPE

However, as the ongoing Octarian War is proving, the Tyranids are encountering ever-greater levels of resistance from their prey. Whilst the Imperium reinforces whole star systems, raising thousands of Imperial Guard regiments and dozens of Space Marine Chapters solely to combat the Tyranid threat, several Eldar craftworlds have begun to burn entire worlds to cinder, employing ancient weapons of destruction not used in millennia. The Tau Empire, having learned well at the claws of Hive Fleet Gorgon, are developing new technologies and weaponry to fight the Tyranids and field-testing experimental prototypes to defend their realm. Even the Necrons and forces of Chaos are turning their attentions towards a foe that is slowly devouring a galaxy that both believe is theirs alone to rule over or despoil as they see fit.

So far these efforts are, at best, succeeding in slowing the Leviathan's rapacious advance, but it is only a matter of time before the Hive Mind adapts. With every lost battle, the hive fleets create new breeds of warrior-organisms and bio-constructs to counter and defeat their foes. Yet with every victory, another world dies, devoured to feed the insatiable hunger of the Hive Mind.

> 'Tyranids are creatures from our darkest nightmares. But remember this; they can bleed and they can die...'
>
> - INQUISITOR KRYPTMAN,
> PRIOR TO HIS EXCOMMUNICATION.

WAR ZONE VALEDOR

There have been times when the starfaring bio-fleets have fallen foul of Warp storms, never to appear again. The splinter fleet of Kraken that was sent headlong into the Empyrean by the seers of Craftworld Iyanden had an even stranger fate. Its bio-ships later emerged from a dimensional rift into the Valedor System, deep in the Segmentum Solar. The splinter fleet had crossed the span of the galaxy in a matter of years. Worse still, it had emerged right in the path of Hive Fleet Leviathan.

When Iyanden's seers learnt of this, panic gripped them. If the bio-matter from Hive Fleet Kraken were to merge with that of Leviathan, the resultant strains of Tyranids would be all but unstoppable, for they would combine the genetic secrets of Ork, Eldar and Human alike. Dreading the repercussions that this unholy union would have upon the craftworlds of the Eldar, the Iyanden council implored their allies on militant Biel-Tan to intercede. Yet despite its swift and deadly attacks, even the Swordwind was unable to keep the hive fleets apart.

If it were not for a shadowy bargain struck with the Dark Eldar, the paradise planet of Valedor – or Dûriel as the Eldar called it – would have been the birth site of a new doom for the galaxy. By using the Fireheart, a Commorrite artefact of incredible power, the combined forces of the Eldar destroyed Dûriel in a storm of fire and violence just as the Tyranids were about to seize their vile prize. In the process they averted disaster – for a time, at least...

FORCES OF THE HIVE MIND

This section details the forces used by the Tyranids – their warriors, their weaponry and the legendary creatures that you can choose to use, including any unique biomorphs that they employ in battle. Each entry describes a unit and gives the specific rules you will need in order to use it in your games. The Tyranid Swarm (pages 92-103) refers back to these entries.

TYRANIDS SPECIAL RULES

The Tyranids army uses a number of special rules that are common to several of its units. These are collected and explained here, in full, for your convenience. Special rules that are unique to particular units are presented in the relevant entry instead. Other, more common, rules are simply listed by name – these are described in full in the Special Rules section of your *Warhammer 40,000* rulebook.

INSTINCTIVE BEHAVIOUR

Unless controlled or coordinated by the domineering will of the Hive Mind, many Tyranid organisms will revert to their baser instincts.

This special rule is always followed, in brackets, by a type: either Lurk, Hunt or Feed, which corresponds to a table opposite. At the beginning of each of your turns, all *Codex: Tyranids* units with this special rule that are outside of the synapse range of any friendly Synapse Creatures (see below) must take a Leadership test unless they are: engaged in combat, falling back, have gone to ground or arrived from reserve this turn. If the test is passed, the unit acts normally during this turn. If the test is failed, the unit must roll a D6 on the appropriate Instinctive Behaviour table. The effects of the result rolled last until the beginning of your next turn, unless specified otherwise.

SHADOW IN THE WARP

The unfathomable presence of the Hive Mind radiates out from its synapse creatures, smothering the ability of the psykers who stand before them to draw upon their mystic powers.

All enemy units and models with the Psyker, Psychic Pilot or Brotherhood of Psykers special rules suffer a -3 penalty to their Leadership whilst they are within 12" of one or more models with the Shadow in the Warp special rule.

SYNAPSE CREATURE

Some Tyranids serve as synaptic conduits or nodal relays through which a portion of the Hive Mind's iron will flows, overriding the natural instincts of the swarm.

Models with the Synapse Creature special rule have a synapse range of 12". Friendly *Codex: Tyranids* models within this synapse range, including the Synapse Creatures themselves, have the Fearless special rule. If a unit from *Codex: Tyranids* is falling back and at least one of the unit's models is within a friendly Synapse Creature's synapse range before the unit moves, the unit automatically Regroups.

WARLORD TRAITS

When generating its Warlord Traits, a Tyranid Warlord may either roll on one of the Warlord Traits tables in the *Warhammer 40,000* rulebook, or instead roll on the Warlord Traits table presented here.

WARLORD TRAITS TABLE

D6	WARLORD TRAIT
1	**Nature's Bane:** *Clouds of microscopic Tyranid organisms swarm around this Warlord, inveigling their way into local flora and creating flesh-eating horrors.* At the beginning each of your Movement phases, you may select one forest, jungle or wood terrain piece within 12" of your Warlord. That terrain piece becomes a Carnivorous Jungle (see the Mysterious Forest table in the *Warhammer 40,000* rulebook) and remains so for the remainder of the game, even if it was previously a different type of forest.
2	**Heightened Senses:** *This Warlord can sense its prey in pitch blackness or through dense smoke.* The Warlord, and all friendly models from *Codex: Tyranids* within 12" of it, have the Night Vision special rule.
3	**Synaptic Lynchpin:** *This Warlord is a strong link in the synapse chain, enacting the Hive Mind's will.* The Warlord's synapse range is 18".
4	**Mind Eater:** *This Warlord devours the minds of enemy leaders and generals so that the Hive Mind can absorb its prey's memories, learn its strategies and adapt its own battle plans accordingly.* Your army gains 2 Victory Points for each enemy model with the Independent Character special rule slain by your Warlord in a challenge. Killing an Independent Character as the result of a sweeping advance does not award these Victory Points.
5	**Digestive Denial:** *This Warlord can ascertain a site that will prove strategically important to its prey, and then compel acidic digestion pools to develop beneath it.* After deployment, but before Scout redeployments and Infiltrate deployments, nominate one piece of terrain in the enemy deployment zone (this may not be one your opponent has purchased as part of their army). The terrain piece's cover save is reduced by one for the duration of the game (to a minimum of 6+). Note that a piece of terrain can only be affected by this ability once.
6	**Adaptive Biology:** *This Warlord has been created to adapt against the weaponry used by the current prey world's defenders.* If the Warlord suffers one or more unsaved Wounds, it gains the Feel No Pain (5+) special rule at the beginning of its next Movement phase and keeps it for the remainder of the game.

INSTINCTIVE BEHAVIOUR TABLES

INSTINCTIVE BEHAVIOUR (LURK)

D6	LURK RESULT
1-3	**Survive:** *The Tyranids' survival instincts take over and they turn tail and flee the battlefield.* The unit is treated as having failed a Morale test and must immediately Fall Back.
4-5	**Seek Cover:** *The brood immediately seeks out shelter to hide from the enemy, ignoring the foe until they are safely concealed from their eyes.* In the Movement phase, the unit is not slowed by difficult terrain, though its models must take Dangerous Terrain tests as normal. In the Shooting phase, the unit can Run, but it can only shoot if it is in a building or area terrain (if the unit is partially within area terrain, only those models within area terrain are allowed to shoot). The unit cannot charge in the Assault phase.
6	**Stalk:** *The Tyranids blend seamlessly into the shadows, stalking their prey from safety until the right time to strike presents itself.* This follows all the rules for Seek Cover (above). In addition, the unit gains the Stealth special rule.

INSTINCTIVE BEHAVIOUR (HUNT)

D6	HUNT RESULT
1-3	**Burrow and Hide:** *Without the Hive Mind's direction, the brood burrows to protect itself from enemy fire.* The unit immediately Goes to Ground. Units that contain at least one model with the Fearless special rule treat this result as Prowl (below), instead.
4-5	**Prowl:** *The Tyranids' instincts take over and they advance in search of foes to hunt with their bio-weapons.* In the Shooting phase, the unit cannot Run and must instead shoot at the closest enemy unit that is within range and line of sight of at least one model in the Tyranid unit. If there is no viable target, the Tyranid unit can do nothing during the Shooting phase. The unit cannot charge in the Assault phase.
6	**Destroy:** *The brood catches the scent of fresh prey on the wind and they become hyper-actively agitated, bio-weapons spitting death until the prey is utterly destroyed.* This follows all the rules for Prowl (above). In addition, the unit gains the Preferred Enemy special rule.

INSTINCTIVE BEHAVIOUR (FEED)

D6	FEED RESULT
1-3	**Cannibalistic Hunger:** *On the verge of starvation and desperate to sate their gnawing hunger, the Tyranids turn upon themselves.* The unit immediately suffers a number of hits equal to the number of models in that unit. These hits are resolved using the unit's majority Strength (if drawn, use the highest) and AP-. Wounds are allocated by the owning player and armour saves (but not cover saves) may be taken. After resolving casualties (if any) the unit can do nothing else until the end of its turn. Units consisting of only a single model treat this result as Devour (below), instead.
4-5	**Devour:** *Driven by their instincts, the Tyranids hurl themselves at the closest prey they can find, teeth and claws eager to bite into flesh.* In the Shooting phase, the unit cannot shoot or Run. In the Assault phase, if the unit is able to declare a charge, it must do so against the closest viable enemy unit. If the unit cannot declare a charge, it does nothing in the Assault phase.
6	**Kill:** *The brood's ravenous hunger sends them into a murderous frenzy.* This follows all the rules for Devour (above). In addition, the unit gains the Rage special rule.

HIVE TYRANTS

Hive Tyrants are the commanders of the Tyranid swarms and enact the Hive Mind's will on the field of battle. Though individuals display a wide variety of physical characteristics, all Hive Tyrants are fearsome hulking monsters that tower over even a Dreadnought. They are brutally strong, able to shatter ferrocrete with sickening ease. Every part of such a beast's body is perfectly created to kill, even the layers of chitinous plating that protect them. A Hive Tyrant is a formidable opponent at any distance, as deadly with ranged weapons as it is with bonesword or claw.

Hive Tyrants are highly psychic, and their relationship to the Hive Mind is amongst the closest of any known bioform. Indeed, the synaptic link is so strong that they are the primary conduits through which the Hive Mind enforces its dominance over a hive fleet's lesser creatures. The instinctive nature of a Tyranid swarm is smothered with implacable drive and purpose, and the need to hunt and devour is imbued with a cunning and tactical awareness that would put the galaxy's finest strategists to shame.

Hive Tyrants were created not only to overpower their prey, but also to outthink it. Unlike many Tyranid creatures, Hive Tyrants are incredibly intelligent and are even, to some extent, self-aware. Whilst they are still slaved to the gestalt consciousness of the Hive Mind, they are given wider latitude in achieving its goals. As such, they can respond to battlefield events far faster than the inscrutable Hive Mind and adapt the behaviour of the swarms they command accordingly. As a result of their highly developed synaptic connection and greater levels of intelligence, Hive Tyrants are also able to manifest potent psychic powers. By harnessing tiny slivers of the Hive Mind's terrifying will, Hive Tyrants can invigorate the swarm, shatter their foe's morale or shred the minds of their prey.

Hive Tyrants embody the Tyranid Hive Mind completely, but their destruction does not in any way diminish it. Death is simply another learning experience that gives insight to the prey's strengths and weaknesses. This goes some way to explain why the Tyranids can rarely be defeated the same way twice. Should a Hive Tyrant be slain on the battlefield, the Hive Mind simply grows a replacement, imbuing it with the same knowledge as its predecessor. Fortunately for the rest of the galaxy, this does not lead to infallibility of purpose. Even the most fearsome Hive Tyrant cannot anticipate its prey's every ploy, nor can it oversee every quarter of the battlefield. However, the Hive Mind's capacity to regrow its fallen leaders does render each Hive Tyrant practically immortal. No matter how many times a Hive Tyrant is killed, sooner or later it will always come back to overcome and devour its prey.

	WS	BS	S	T	W	I	A	Ld	Sv
Hive Tyrant	8	4	6	6	4	5	4	10	3+

UNIT TYPE: Monstrous Creature (Character).

WEAPONS & BIOMORPHS:
Two pairs of scything talons (pg 63).

SPECIAL RULES: Psyker (Mastery Level 2),
Shadow in the Warp (pg 38), **Synapse Creature** (pg 38).

PSYKER: A Hive Tyrant generates its psychic powers from the **Powers of the Hive Mind** (pg 69).

UPGRADES:
Hive Commander: For each Hive Tyrant in your army with this upgrade, choose a single troops selection from the same detachment. All models in the selected unit gain the Outflank special rule.

Indescribable Horror: Units taking a Fear test caused by this model must roll an extra dice when taking the test and use the highest two results. In most circumstances, this will mean the unit rolls 3D6 and discards the lowest dice roll.

Old Adversary: This Hive Tyrant re-rolls all failed To Hit and To Wound rolls of 1 when fighting in close combat.

TYRANID WARRIORS

Tyranid Warriors are the most adaptable of all the Hive Mind's bioforms. They are creatures from the blackest of nightmares, unstoppable killing machines with pulsing ichor for blood, needle-sharp teeth and darkly gleaming eyes that reveal a terrible intelligence at work. A Tyranid Warrior stands twice the height of a man, its carapace protected by a thick chitin. One might expect such a creature to be slow in its actions, but a Tyranid Warrior is lithe, with reactions as swift as a whip.

Tyranid Warriors have the mental flexibility to employ a wide variety of bio-weapon symbiotes. As such, on the battlefield, they can be found leading all areas of a Tyranid swarm: fighting in close quarters with claws, boneswords and lash whips, or at longer ranges with devourers, deathspitters or even heavier bio-cannons. Whatever weaponry it wields, a Tyranid Warrior is a dangerous and unforgiving foe, able to identify and exploit the weaknesses of its targets with innate shrewdness. Worse, with its alien consciousness permanently bonded to the ageless Hive Mind, a Tyranid Warrior can instantly draw upon a reservoir of knowledge and experience that spans epochs, should its own prove insufficient to the task at hand.

Though they are formidable fighters in their own right, it is the Tyranid Warriors' role as the synaptic lynchpins of the swarm that makes them truly deadly. Tyranid Warriors are psychic resonators for the unwavering will of the Hive Mind and some of the more common conduits used to exert control over the less receptive creatures of the hive fleets. As such, Tyranid Warriors form a vital link in the Tyranid swarm, acting as relays and amplifiers through which Hive Tyrants issue their commands. So crucial is this role to a hive fleet's efforts to defeat a prey world's defenders that each Hive Tyrant is invariably accompanied by several broods of Tyranid Warriors cultured from its very own flesh – the better to enhance the psychic link throughout the swarm. This is not to imply that Tyranid Warriors are merely drones, for each is instinctively capable of assessing local battlefield situations. They can then, if the need arises, direct those Tyranid creatures near them, like an officer marshalling their forces, to exploit any tactical weakness that may appear in the enemy's defences.

TYRANID SHRIKES

Tyranid Shrikes are an adaptation of the Tyranid Warrior bioform, with leathery wings that allow them to swoop and soar through the skies of a prey world. With broods of Tyranid Shrikes at its command, the Hive Mind can ensure that its influence extends to every corner of the swarm, even to the Gargoyles and Harpies whose aerial assaults are prone to leaving them isolated from the rest of the force.

Though more lightly armoured than Tyranid Warriors, Shrikes can redeploy at a moment's notice. In doing so, they can fill gaps in the synaptic web or assail the foe where it is most vulnerable. Few enemies expect so large a creature to approach from the skies, and a well-timed attack by Tyranid Shrikes invariably spells disaster if the prey's sentries are caught off guard.

TYRANID PRIMES

Tyranid Primes are the apex of the Tyranid Warrior strain, faster, stronger and smarter than the other Warriors they lead to battle, who instinctively emulate their deadly skill.

	WS	BS	S	T	W	I	A	Ld	Sv
Tyranid Warrior	5	3	4	4	3	4	3	10	4+
Tyranid Shrike	5	3	4	4	3	4	3	10	5+
Tyranid Prime	6	4	5	5	3	5	4	10	3+

UNIT TYPE: Tyranid Warriors are **Infantry**. Tyranid Shrikes are **Jump Infantry**. Tyranid Primes are **Infantry (Character)**.

WEAPONS & BIOMORPHS: Devourer (pg 64), **scything talons** (pg 63).

SPECIAL RULES:
Independent Character (Tyranid Prime only), **Shadow in the Warp** (pg 38), **Synapse Creature** (pg 38), **Very Bulky.**

Alpha Warrior (Tyranid Prime only): All Tyranid Warriors or Tyranid Shrikes in the same unit as a Tyranid Prime use its Weapon Skill and Ballistic Skill rather than their own, unless their own would be higher for any reason.

GAUNTS

Termagants, Hormagaunts and Gargoyles are simple bioforms created by the hive fleets in their billions. Onslaughts by these creatures often precede the main attack, wave after wave hurling themselves against enemy lines like an avalanche of teeth, claws and bio-weapons fire.

TERMAGANTS

Termagants are agile and cunning creatures. They are amongst the smallest of the Hive Mind's warriors and were originally created to roam the arterial passages of bio-ships in search of intruders. In planetary invasions, Termagants scuttle forwards on four legs whilst unleashing torrents of fire from the anti-personnel bio-weaponry – commonly fleshborers – clutched in their clawed forelimbs.

Termagants are expendable bioforms, and the Hive Mind treats them as such. It is not uncommon for the Hive Mind to suppress the Termagants' survival instincts and send them forwards to die in droves until the enemy's ammunition is depleted, defensive positions are overrun, resistance has been eliminated and victory is assured.

HORMAGAUNTS

Hormagaunts are vicious and extraordinarily single-minded predators that will pursue their victims without pause or respite. With powerful hind legs, Hormagaunts dart across the battlefield in a series of bounding leaps, ignoring injury and tiredness until they have run down their exhausted quarry and torn it apart with frenzied strikes of their scythe-like claws.

Hormagaunts have fearsome hunting instincts and require little direction from the Hive Mind to seek out and slaughter prey. Indeed, once the Tyranid assault begins, they are mostly left to their own devices. On occasion, however, the Hive Mind will make contact with a brood's quicksilver consciousness, spurring it towards a more distant or strategically important foe.

GARGOYLES

A Tyranid attack is preceded by the beating of thousands of membranous wings as Gargoyle broods descend upon the foe, blotting out the sun and spitting death from their fleshborers. Their winged manoeuvrability gives Gargoyles a distinct hunting advantage. Wherever Tyranids attack a planet, the defenders look fearfully to the skies, for they know that every sky-borne shadow could be a flock of Gargoyles about to attack.

Though Gargoyles instinctively hunt at range, many a soldier has mistaken this stand-offish behaviour for cowardice. These fools discover too late just how dangerous Gargoyles can be at close quarters, realising their doom only after the winged creatures spit caustic venom into their eyes. A moment later, blinded and debilitated, the victim is torn apart by a flock of lashing tails and razor talons.

	WS	BS	S	T	W	I	A	Ld	Sv
Termagant	3	3	3	3	1	4	1	6	6+
Hormagaunt	3	3	3	3	1	5	2	6	6+
Gargoyle	3	3	3	3	1	4	1	6	6+

UNIT TYPE: Termagants and Hormagaunts are **Infantry**. Gargoyles are **Jump Infantry**.

WEAPONS & BIOMORPHS:
Termagants: **Fleshborer** (pg 64).

Hormagaunts: **Scything talons** (pg 63).

Gargoyles: **Fleshborer** (pg 64), **blinding venom** (pg 67).

SPECIAL RULES:
Termagants: **Instinctive Behaviour (Lurk)** (pg 38), **Move Through Cover.**

Hormagaunts: **Fleet, Instinctive Behaviour (Feed)** (pg 38), **Move Through Cover.**

Bounding Leap: Units entirely composed of models with this special rule Run an additional 3" (this will normally be D6+3").

Gargoyles: **Instinctive Behaviour (Hunt)** (pg 38).

GENESTEALERS

There are many terrifying creatures in the Tyranid hive fleets, but one in particular has carved out a horrifying and bloody legend on more than a thousand worlds. It is a lurker in dark places, a clawed harbinger of sudden death. It is known as the Genestealer, and it is a plague upon the galaxy.

A Genestealer is a swift and powerful predator with lightning-fast reflexes and serrated claws that can tear through even the thickest of armour. Genestealers also have large, highly adaptive brains and possess a form of brood telepathy that allows them to function with full independence from the Hive Mind. This autonomy allows them to destroy through stealth and guile that which cannot be defeated through numbers alone.

A strong survival instinct drives Genestealers outwards from the hive fleets, and they seek out space-bound vessels attempting to flee the surface of doomed prey-worlds. It is simple for a Genestealer to stow away aboard such ships, nesting unseen amongst crawl-spaces until it is brought to a new planet by the unsuspecting crew. If a single Genestealer reaches an inhabited world, it can spell disaster. Genestealers reproduce by implanting other life forms with their own genetic material. Once infected, a victim is enthralled by the Genestealers' nascent telepathy and Tyranid attributes are passed on to its offspring, creating monstrous hybrids completely under the alien's domination. These deformities eventually breed true, creating 'purestrain' Genestealers under the control of a Broodlord – the strongest and most dangerous of their kind. These Genestealers seem content to lurk in sewers and caves beneath cities, preying on the populace like folktale monsters until the Hive Mind's will once again dominates their minds.

No one knows how widespread the Genestealer infestation has become or how many worlds if affects. For every brood uncovered and purged, a dozen go unnoticed. When a Tyranid hive fleet enters an infested system, the Hive Mind asserts its synaptic dominion over the Broodlord and its clan. Planetary defenders are thrown into disarray as Genestealers suddenly burst from the shadows, overwhelming crucial systems and leaving the prey world vulnerable before the merciless Tyranid onslaught.

YMGARL GENESTEALERS

The Genestealers of Ymgarl were one of the first Tyranid creatures encountered by Mankind, but their origins remain a mystery. They do not seem to have been created by any known hive fleet, leading to speculation that they are the last survivors of a vanguard fleet lost for time immemorial. Whatever the truth, since their discovery on the moons of Ymgarl, every attempt to eradicate them has been met with butchery and failure. Ymgarl Genestealers are unique, in that they can alter their own flesh in a matter of moments. Their claw-tipped fingers can quickly elongate and fuse together to form curved blades to hack apart their enemies. A few seconds later and the same limbs split apart into ropes of sinewy tendon to ensnare victims attempting to escape, dragging them instead towards the writhing mass of tentacles each Ymgarl Genestealer uses to feast upon its prey's blood in place of a fanged maw. Stranger still, whilst the instincts of other Genestealers lead them to flee their parent hive fleets, Ymgarl Genestealers actively seek them out. They spread across the galaxy searching for worlds in the path of an advancing hive fleet. However, the Hive Mind has no wish to reabsorb them, lest their mutable instability spread amongst the hive fleet. Therefore, after a world has been scoured of all other biomass, the Ymgarl brood is left behind to begin their search anew.

	WS	BS	S	T	W	I	A	Ld	Sv
Genestealer	6	0	4	4	1	6	2	10	5+
Broodlord	7	0	5	5	3	7	4	10	4+

UNIT TYPE: Infantry. Broodlord is **Infantry (Character)**.

WEAPONS & BIOMORPHS: Rending claws (pg 63).

SPECIAL RULES: Bulky (Broodlord only), **Fleet, Infiltrate, Move Through Cover, Psyker (Mastery Level 1)** (Broodlord only).

PSYKER: A Broodlord always knows *The Horror* psychic power (pg 69).

LICTORS

The Lictor is a highly specialised development of the Tyranid Warrior bioform, specifically adapted to fill a scout role in the vanguard of the Tyranid advance. Lictors rove ahead of the main body of a swarm, seeking out pockets of resistance to be eradicated and native life forms to be absorbed. Able to move swiftly and without sound through even the densest terrain, and concealed by a chameleonic carapace that renders it all but invisible to the naked eye, a Lictor can remain hidden until it chooses to strike. It can wait motionless for days, unnoticed by its victims, an unseen herald of approaching disaster.

Lictors are not instinctively aggressive, as they are created primarily to locate prey for the wider swarm. Lictors are opportunistic hunters and therefore tend to stalk their quarry from the shadows, avoiding confrontations where they would be vastly outmatched. A Lictor will often pick off its prey in ones and twos whilst they are separated from their comrades, sometimes retreating for days at a time before launching a further attack.

When the time comes to strike, Lictors are brutally efficient, with a whole arsenal of bio-weaponry that includes mantis-like claws, talons that can pierce steel, barbed flesh hooks and feeder tendrils. The feeder tendrils are tipped with sharpened bony plates that can pierce a victim's skull as easily as they poke through eyeballs and the sockets behind. They are used to lobotomise victims so that the Lictor can swiftly devour its brain and absorb its memories. Thus, in death, the enemy reveals more to a Lictor than it ever did in life, betraying the whereabouts of comrades and exposing any weaknesses that might be exploited.

Yet fearsome as the Lictor is as a physical foe, it has an altogether more deadly purpose than simple slaughter. Stalking Lictors exude a pheromone trail which draws other Tyranids; the larger the concentration of prey, the stronger the response and the more irresistible the lure. So it is that even killing a Lictor is no guarantee of survival, for the creature's mere presence ensures that the swarm already knows where its prey can be found. After that, it's only a matter of time...

	WS	BS	S	T	W	I	A	Ld	Sv
Lictor	6	3	6	4	3	6	3	10	5+

UNIT TYPE: Infantry.

WEAPONS & BIOMORPHS: Rending claws (pg 63), **scything talons** (pg 63), **flesh hooks** (pg 67).

SPECIAL RULES: Deep Strike, Fear, Fleet, Hit & Run, Infiltrate, Instinctive Behaviour (Lurk) (pg 38), **Move Through Cover, Stealth, Very Bulky.**

Chameleonic Skin: A Lictor does not scatter when arriving from Deep Strike Reserve.

Pheromone Trail: If a friendly unit from *Codex: Tyranids* arrives on the battlefield via Deep Strike, it will not scatter so long as the first model in the unit is placed within 6" of a model with this special rule. Note that the model with the Pheromone Trail special rule must already be on the table at the start of the turn for this ability to be used.

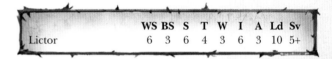

DOMINATRIX

The Dominatrix is a colossal creature of the Tyranid swarm. It is a fearsome opponent, for its sheer mass and panoply of bio-weaponry dwarf that of an Imperial super-heavy tank.

The Dominatrix is no unthinking beast – its level of intelligence is akin to that of the Hive Tyrant, and its link to the Hive Mind surpasses even those mighty creatures. Whilst within range of the Dominatrix's psychic aura, lesser Tyranid creatures become little more than an extension of the Dominatrix's will.

As a result, a swarm under the Dominatrix's direct supervision functions with uncanny efficiency and a tactical genius that is beyond compare. Fortunately, such beasts are extremely rare in all but the most advanced Tyranid swarm, for where the Dominatrix treads, doom surely follows.

ZOANTHROPES

Zoanthropes are created solely to harness the psychic potential of the Hive Mind, and their entire bodies are perfected towards such a function. If necessary, a Zoanthrope can be used to extend the range of the Hive Mind's synaptic control, utilising the beast's vast cerebral capacity to relay its instructions to lesser creatures. Under these circumstances, the Zoanthrope is little more than a highly sophisticated messenger, but this is only a fraction of what their alien minds are capable of. A Zoanthrope's link to the synaptic web is such that, by flexing the merest part of its mind, it can rain incandescent power on the enemy, projecting destructive bolts of energy that boils through adamantium plate and disintegrates flesh with equal ease.

Despite their instinctive command over their otherworldly abilities, tapping into the Hive Mind's psychic potential is not without danger. It is not unknown for Zoanthropes to suffer massive cerebral trauma whilst attempting to harness the energies they wield. In such instances, a surge of psychic power courses through the Zoanthrope, and as the raw energy flows through its mind, synapses overload and burn every neuron in its brain. The creature has just the time to emit a psychic howl of agony before falling limp to the ground, like a puppet whose strings have been severed.

Zoanthropes are vital nodes for harnessing the Hive Mind's psychic might and are created with a powerful sense of self-preservation. Therefore, they instinctively project a potent Warp field to protect themselves in battle – a mental shield that is invisible but for a slight shimmer when small-arms and heavy-weapons fire alike patters harmlessly against it. However, Zoanthropes are still predators, capable of eliminating any perceived threat with bolts of flaming psychic energy.

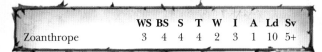

	WS	BS	S	T	W	I	A	Ld	Sv
Zoanthrope	3	4	4	4	2	3	1	10	5+

UNIT TYPE: Infantry.

SPECIAL RULES: Brotherhood of Psykers, Shadow in the Warp (pg 38), **Synapse Creature** (pg 38), **Very Bulky.**

Psychic Brood: A Zoanthrope brood follows all the rules for Brotherhood of Psykers except that the unit has a Mastery Level of 2. In addition, if a brood of Zoanthropes uses the *Warp Blast* power (pg 69), the number of shots fired is equal to the number of Zoanthropes in that brood.

For example, a brood of three Zoanthropes that successfully manifested Warp Blast *would treat both the Burst and Lance profiles as Assault 3.*

Warp Field: Zoanthropes have a 3+ invulnerable save.

PSYKER: A Zoanthrope brood always knows the *Warp Blast* psychic power (pg 69). The unit can generate one additional power from the **Powers of the Hive Mind** (pg 69).

THE DOOM OF MALAN'TAI

The Eldar legend of the Doom of Malan'tai refers not only to the tale of an entire craftworld's death, but also to the abominable Tyranid creature that caused it – to the Eldar, the two are indistinguishable. The lament speaks of a Tyranid creature unlike any other, a beast that gorged not upon flesh and blood, but upon the life-force of its victims, leaving only soulless oblivion in its wake. The Doom of Malan'tai was an adaptation of the Zoanthrope, and its weak physical appearance belied its true horror. So it was that, when a lone, wounded bio-ship invaded Craftworld Malan'tai, the Eldar did not at first realise that the true threat lay not with the towering Tyranid monsters rampaging through their home, but with the unassuming creature left relatively unhindered to feed on Eldar souls. As it fed, the Doom of Malan'tai's power grew, the absorbed life-energy enhancing its fearsome psychic might. Once it had gorged on the spirits of the craftworld's infinity circuit, it was nigh invulnerable, possessing the power to pulp Eldar warriors, snap wraithbone war-constructs and shatter towering spires with cataclysmic bolts of psychic energy. It was all that the few Eldar survivors could do to escape Malan'tai, a craftworld found adrift in space years later, reduced to nought but a cold, lifeless shell. Of the loathsome creature that had brought about its destruction, there was no sign...

TYRANID GUARDS

While many Tyranid creations are expendable, others are vital to a hive fleet's success. To this end, the Hive Mind has created a number of organisms whose sole role on the battlefield is the safeguarding and protection of other Tyranid bioforms.

TYRANT GUARD

Tyrant Guard are the ultimate bodyguards; it is the entire purpose of their creation. Their instincts tend not towards self-preservation, but to the defence of the Hive Tyrant to which they are bonded. Should the Hive Tyrant come under attack, its Tyrant Guard move into the path of incoming fire without thought or concern, sheltering their charge with their own bodies. Tyrant Guard, therefore, take the form of colossal living shields. They are all but impervious to small-arms fire, and should heavy weaponry be brought to bear, several salvoes are required to fell even one of these beasts. These creatures have an incredible resistance to injury and are only dimly aware of pain, shrugging off wounds that would blow a man apart.

Should their charge be slain, the Tyrant Guard will go berserk, lashing out and tearing at the enemy with brutal ferocity and savage abandon. A Tyrant Guard's rampage is not guided by grief, nor a sense of neglected duty, for such things are alien concepts to the Tyranids. Rather, a Tyrant Guard's reaction is pure instinct and part of the coldly calculated strategy of the Hive Mind. Hive Tyrants are vital to the Tyranid onslaught, and if the enemy finds a way to bring such a beast down, the Hive Mind does not want knowledge of how the feat was accomplished to survive the battle and be passed on to a future foe.

HIVE GUARD

In the later stages of a Tyranid invasion, strange alien architecture begins to blight the prey world. Towering spore chimneys burst from beneath the churned ground to belch their poisonous spores into the air, and capillary towers are grown to funnel the digested gruel of the planet's biomass up to the Hive Ships waiting in space. Such structures are vital to the Tyranids' attempt to consume a world, and the Hive Mind has created a specific beast for their protection – the Hive Guard.

Hive Guard are heavily armoured gun-beasts bound to extremely powerful symbiotic bio-weapons. Though they have no eyes, Hive Guard possess a weak telepathic ability that allows them to perceive through the senses of other Tyranids, giving them access to a wealth of targeting information that would overwhelm even the most sophisticated technological cogitator. The scant mental capacity apportioned to the Hive Guard means that, without the direction of the Hive Mind, they have been known to stand motionless, waiting for prey to come within range instead of moving forwards to engage.

	WS	BS	S	T	W	I	A	Ld	Sv
Tyrant Guard	5	3	5	6	2	4	2	7	3+
Hive Guard	4	3	5	6	2	2	2	7	4+

UNIT TYPE: Infantry.

WEAPONS & BIOMORPHS:
Tyrant Guard: **Rending claws** (pg 63), **scything talons** (pg 63).

Hive Guard: **Impaler cannon** (pg 64).

SPECIAL RULES:
Tyrant Guard: **Instinctive Behaviour (Feed)** (pg 38), **Very Bulky.**

Blind Rampage: If a Hive Tyrant (or the Swarmlord) is killed whilst part of a unit of Tyrant Guard (see the Shieldwall special rule, below), from the end of that turn the surviving Tyrant Guard have the Furious Charge and Rage special rules for the remainder of the battle.

Shieldwall: A single Hive Tyrant (or the Swarmlord) may join a unit of Tyrant Guard exactly as if it were an Independent Character. A Hive Tyrant (or the Swarmlord) in a unit that contains at least one model with this special rule automatically passes Look Out, Sir rolls.

Hive Guard: **Instinctive Behaviour (Hunt)** (pg 38), **Very Bulky.**

VENOMTHROPES

Venomthropes are gangrel creatures with scrawny bodies and whip-like tentacles that drip with alien poisons. Their carapaces house bulging, gas-filled bladders, allowing the Venomthropes to float ponderously across the battlefield, using their clusters of tendrils to steer themselves towards suitable prey.

In addition to providing the Venomthropes' mobility, the gas bladders also produce thick clouds of alien spores. Venomthropes are shrouded in a dense fog of these airborne spores that conceals not only them, but any other broods of Tyranid predators advancing in their wake. The spores are also the Venomthropes' most insidious form of attack, for they are extremely poisonous to non-Tyranid life forms. Brief exposure causes violent bouts of nausea and uncontrollable muscle spasms, leaving foes weakened and easy prey for the nearby Tyranids. If the enemy is unfortunate, or foolish enough to inhale the Venomthropes' emissions for any prolonged period, the alien spores will gain a foothold within the foe's body. Reproducing rapidly, they spread throughout the host's system, breaking down organic tissues at a horrifying rate. The victim ultimately drowns in its own frothing and infected bodily fluids, and as the diseased corpse collapses in on itself, the Venomthrope uses its feeder tendrils to suck up the bubbling remains.

The bodies of Venomthropes are coated in a variety of alien poisons, but it is their writhing tentacles that exude the most lethal of all Tyranid toxins. These venoms are so virulent that on contact, they cause the flesh of their prey to wither and slough from bone. Those victims that do not succumb immediately are entangled by the writhing limbs, bound in a poisonous embrace until the Venomthropes toxic spores do their gruesome work.

Though Venomthropes are not the most physically imposing or aggressive Tyranid bioforms, they are, if anything, more dangerous to a prey world's continued survival than hordes of warrior organisms. Left to their own devices, a single brood of Venomthropes will eventually poison not only the entire world's indigenous life, but also its soil and atmosphere, leaving the plague-shrouded planet fit only for consumption by the hive fleet.

	WS	BS	S	T	W	I	A	Ld	Sv
Venomthrope	3	3	4	4	2	3	2	6	5+

UNIT TYPE: Infantry.

WEAPONS & BIOMORPHS: Lash whips (pg 63), **toxic miasma** (pg 67).

SPECIAL RULES: Instinctive Behaviour (Lurk) (pg 38), **Poisoned (2+), Shrouded, Very Bulky.**

Spore Cloud: All friendly models from *Codex: Tyranids* that are within 6" of at least one Venomthrope have the Shrouded special rule.

MALANTHROPES

Malanthropes are rarely seen Tyranid creatures. This is because they are not truly warrior organisms, and so are not usually encountered by a prey world's defenders. Instead, these floating creatures follow behind the Tyranid attack; they are typically created only after a prey world's protectors have been defeated and the swarm is in the process of devouring the planet's biomass. On those few occasions that a survivor has seen a Malanthrope and somehow escaped, they have brought with them a tale of horror. They describe creatures superficially similar in appearance to Venomthropes, but far larger and more terrifying. They report seeing these giants drift across corpse-strewn battlefields, but unlike other Tyranids, which mindlessly devour everything in their way, Malanthropes seem to selectively search through the slain – as to what they are searching for, none can say. Once a morsel that suits their taste has been found, they grasp hold of the body with long groping tendrils before feeding the entire mass into their tentacled maw with small, dextrous arms. Those unfortunate enough to still be alive when caught by a Malanthrope are stung with a paralysing toxin and then swallowed whole. Living and awake, but trapped within the Malanthrope's bloated digestion sacs, the skin, flesh and bones of these victims is slowly absorbed over the following days – a terrible and excruciatingly painful death.

TERVIGONS

The Tervigon is a massive synapse creature whose towering carapace shields a swollen abdomen. Though possessed of a formidable array of bio-weapons, from monstrous claws that crush any prey that ventures too close, to banks of razor-tipped spines that can be fired a considerable distance, the Tervigon's true threat lies within...

Every Tervigon serves as a living incubator, within whose bloated form dozens upon dozens of Termagants slumber in a state of near-life. The Tervigon can spawn its dormant broods at will, jolting their minds into wakefulness. So it is that a foe engaging a Tervigon up close will find itself assailed by waves of skittering Termagants. Such a confrontation is terrible to behold, for a Tervigon's capacity to reinforce is vast, and its broods are driven into a near-frenzy by the need to protect their progenitor. The only way for a cool-headed enemy commander to end the horror is to have his troops concentrate all their firepower on the Tervigon. If the beast is slain, the resultant synaptic backlash may kill many of its young. Such a tactic is easier said than done, for the firepower needed to fell a Tervigon is comparable to that needed to demolish a heavily armoured battle fortress.

When a hive fleet travels through space, Tervigons do not slumber in a dormant state like the majority of other Tyranids. Instead, they roam the ship's cavernous innards.

Should a Tervigon detect intruders, it immediately spawns a veritable army of Termagants to repulse the foe whilst using its potent synaptic powers to hamper the enemy further or else awaken additional warriors. Unless the foe can act quickly, they will quickly be engulfed and overwhelmed beneath a tide of drooling jaws and serrated claws.

	WS	BS	S	T	W	I	A	Ld	Sv
Tervigon	3	3	5	6	6	2	3	10	3+

UNIT TYPE: Monstrous Creature.

WEAPONS & BIOMORPHS: Scything talons (pg 63), **stinger salvo** (pg 65).

SPECIAL RULES: Psyker (Mastery Level 1), Shadow in the Warp (pg 38), **Synapse Creature** (pg 38).

Brood Progenitor: All Termagants in units within 12" of the Tervigon have the Counter-attack special rule.

Spawn Termagants: At the end of your Movement phase, a Tervigon can spawn Termagants (see army list, pg 96), even if it is locked in close combat. If it does so, roll 3D6 – this is the number of models spawned. Place the new unit of Termagants on the table so that it is wholly within 6" of the Tervigon. Models in this new unit cannot be placed in impassable terrain or within 1" of enemy models. If you cannot place some of the models due to the restrictions above or because you have run out of Termagant models, the excess is discarded.

The spawned unit cannot move during the Movement phase in which it is spawned, nor can it charge this turn, but it is free to shoot or Run as normal. A unit spawned by a Tervigon is identical in every way to a Termagant unit chosen from the Troops section of the army list, and is treated as such for all mission special rules. Models in a spawned unit are armed with fleshborers and may not purchase options.

If any double is rolled when determining the size of a spawned unit, the Tervigon has temporarily exhausted its supply of larvae – the Termagant unit is created as normal, but the Tervigon cannot spawn any further units for the rest of the game.

Synaptic Backlash: If a Tervigon is slain, roll 3D6 before removing the model as a casualty. Each friendly unit of Termagants within 12" of the Tervigon immediately suffers a number of Strength 3 AP- hits equal to the result. Cover saves may not be taken against these hits and Wounds are allocated as per shooting, with the Tervigon as the firer. After all Termagant casualties have been resolved (if any), remove the Tervigon from play.

PSYKER: A Tervigon generates its psychic powers from the **Powers of the Hive Mind** (pg 69).

RAVENERS

Raveners are voracious predators, their clawed and snake-like bodies driven onwards by an all-consuming hunger. Twisted musculature grants these beasts a terrifying turn of speed. Raveners can bound over small obstacles in an eye-blink, dart between larger obstructions and even slither through flooded marshland with bewildering swiftness. Yet such is not the Raveners' only form of approach and neither is it the most feared, for at least when these alien horrors are charging their prey down across the battlefield, the enemy has a chance to see their doom. The power housed within the Raveners' wiry forms allows them to burrow long distances beneath a world's surface, before emerging in a spray of earth right in front of an enemy position, claws eviscerating their ambushed prey whilst their thorax-mounted weapon symbiotes spit death.

	WS	BS	S	T	W	I	A	Ld	Sv
Ravener	5	3	4	4	3	5	3	6	5+

UNIT TYPE: Beasts.

WEAPONS & BIOMORPHS:
Two pairs of scything talons (pg 63).

SPECIAL RULES: Deep Strike,
Instinctive Behaviour (Feed) (pg 38), **Very Bulky.**

THE RED TERROR

	WS	BS	S	T	W	I	A	Ld	Sv
The Red Terror	6	3	5	5	3	5	4	8	4+

For twenty days, the so-called Red Terror preyed upon the defenders of the Imperial mining world of Devlan Primus. Survivors spoke of a beast with a blood-coloured carapace, talons that could tunnel through rockcrete, and a maw so wide it could swallow a man whole. With every re-telling, the legends grew more fearsome and terrifying. Some claimed that the Red Terror was the size of a Ravener; others swore it was as big as a Trygon. The survivors of the Devlan massacre may well have mistaken the attacks of several such creatures for those of a single beast. However, if the Red Terror is a distinct Tyranid organism, it must be a highly efficient killer; it has never been reported since, but this can only be because there have been no survivors left to tell the tale.

'Emperor knows what pit spawned the hideous apparition we came to know as the Red Terror. It first attacked the outer bastion and twenty-four men died before we drove it away with flamers. We never even found the bodies of Lieutenant Borales and Captain Lowe, just a trail of slime that led away from the command post and into the tunnels. It returned the following night, and the slaughter began anew, but this time we were ready for it... or so we thought.'
- FROM 'TWENTY DAYS IN HELL,
THE RETREAT FROM DEVLAN PRIMUS'

UNIT TYPE: Beast (Character).

WEAPONS & BIOMORPHS:
Two pairs of scything talons (pg 63),
prehensile pincer (pg 67).

SPECIAL RULES: Deep Strike,
Instinctive Behaviour (Feed) (pg 38), **Very Bulky.**

Swallow Whole: If the Red Terror hits with at least four of its close combat attacks in a single phase (excluding its prehensile pincer attack), you may nominate a single enemy Infantry, Jump Infantry or Jet Pack Infantry model in base contact with the Red Terror and attempt to swallow it whole.

If you choose to do so, no To Wound rolls are made for any of the Red Terror's Attacks (excluding its prehensile pincer attack). Instead, the nominated model must pass a single invulnerable save (if it has one) or be removed from play as a casualty. There is no need to decide beforehand if you will attempt to swallow a model whole; declare after rolling To Hit. Enemy models with either the Very Bulky or Extremely Bulky special rule cannot be nominated as targets to be Swallowed Whole. If no models in the target unit can be nominated, the Red Terror cannot choose to Swallow Whole and must roll To Wound normally.

TYRANID ARTILLERY ORGANISMS

Whilst many Tyranid organisms excel at tearing their prey apart at close quarters, the Hive Mind has created several with the express purpose of destroying its foes from a great distance. Biovores are perhaps the most commonly encountered 'living artillery' bioform utilised by the hive fleets, but larger and stranger creatures bearing highly specialised bio-cannons are becoming increasingly prevalent. They are not only powerful weapons in the Hive Mind's arsenal, but proof of the Tyranid's highly adaptive nature.

BIOVORES

A Biovore is a squat, bloated creature – yet no less deadly for all that. Deep within its lumpen form, the Biovore nurtures a clutch of Spore Mines – living bombs that blanket the enemy in acids, poisons and shrapnel-sized pieces of chitin. Biovores thump forward in battle, bony protrusions on their fore-limbs anchoring themselves into the ground as they release their vile payload in a single shuddering spasm.

As the Spore Mine is flung through the air, its internal gas bladder inflates and it floats down towards ground level. Even if the shot misses its initial target, the danger it poses is far from over; for the Spore Mine is possessed of a rudimentary intelligence and detonates not on impact with the ground, but when it senses the proximity of a non-Tyranid life form.

SPORE MINE CLUSTERS

Clusters of Spore Mines are often seeded directly onto worlds from orbiting bio-ships. Spore Mines have been known to drift for days, just waiting for an unwary foe to come near, before detonating with brutal effect.

	WS	BS	S	T	W	I	A	Ld	Sv
Biovore	3	3	4	4	3	2	2	6	4+
Spore Mine	-	-	1	1	1	1	-	1	-

UNIT TYPE: Infantry.

WEAPONS & BIOMORPHS:
Biovore: **Spore Mine launcher** (pg 65).

SPECIAL RULES:
Biovore: **Instinctive Behaviour (Hunt)** (pg 38), **Very Bulky.**

Spore Mine: **Deep Strike, Fearless, Floating Death** (pg 65), **Living Bomb** (pg 65).

Designer's Note: *The full rules for Spore Mines can be found on page 65, in the Weapons and Biomorphs section.*

EXOCRINES

Exocrines are feared for their ability to deal death from afar. The most distinctive feature of an Exocrine is its dorsal bio-cannon, which emits a high-pitched hiss a second before firing, giving its prey just enough time to realise the danger they are in before searing plasma scours them into atoms.

The Exocrine is purely a means of transportation for the weapon symbiote nested into its flesh. Whilst the Exocrine possesses considerable strength, it has a disproportionately small brain. Indeed, the dorsal bio-weapon has a larger mental capacity than its host and often diverts a portion of its own intelligence to subsume the Exocrine's will. Only when the larger beast remains still can the symbiote focus all of its mental resources into targeting and destroying its prey.

	WS	BS	S	T	W	I	A	Ld	Sv
Exocrine	3	3	6	6	5	3	3	7	3+

UNIT TYPE: Monstrous Creature.

WEAPONS & BIOMORPHS: Bio-plasmic cannon (pg 64), **scything talons** (pg 63).

SPECIAL RULES: Fearless, Instinctive Behaviour (Hunt) (pg 38).

Symbiotic Targeting: If an Exocrine does not move in its Movement phase, it gains a +1 bonus to its Ballistic Skill until the end of its turn. An Exocrine cannot declare a charge during the same turn that it uses this special rule.

TYRANID FEEDER ORGANISMS

The hive fleets create many organisms whose sole role is the consumption of biomass. Whilst the Ripper is the simplest and most numerous of such creatures, the Hive Mind has also created several larger species of feeder-beast, creatures that can speed up the digestion of a prey world tenfold, pre-digesting biomass and devouring in one bite what would take hundreds of smaller jaws to tear apart.

Being larger, stronger and often created with deadly symbiotic bio-weapons, these specialised feeder-beasts can also be deployed before a prey world's defences have been completely defeated. Thus, they are often encountered amongst the rearguard of Tyranid attacks, hunting down the last remnants of resistance from a planet's populace alongside other warrior-organisms before stripping the battlefield clean of corpses the moment a battle is won.

HARUSPEXES

The Tyranid Haruspex is a ferocious beast created to consume biomass at a sickening pace. It is possessed of a rapacious appetite, driven by the need to sate an infinite hunger. Few foes are foolish enough to stand before a feeding Haruspex, for it can devour an entire platoon of soldiers in a matter of moments, shovelling victim after victim into its craw without ever slowing down. Any morsel that proves too large to be swallowed in one gulp is seized with the Haruspex's gargantuan claws and ripped, crushed or battered apart with negligent ease. Buildings are smashed open, battle tanks torn asunder and the unfortunate prey sheltering inside hungrily devoured. Only those that turn and flee have any hope of survival, and only then if they can avoid the Haruspex's grasping tongue as it lashes out to grab hold of its prey and drag it, kicking and screaming, into its vast maw.

PYROVORES

Pyrovores exist to pre-digest biomass; their maws drip with acids that reduce flesh, metal and even stone to a smouldering mucous for consumption by other Tyranids. A Pyrovore's primary threat is its dorsal bio-weapon, which can launch searing flames to reduce its foes to ash. Slaying a Pyrovore is not without risk either, for its deathblow can ignite volatile ichors within its stomachs in an explosion that leaves behind only charred scraps of flesh and a foul smell.

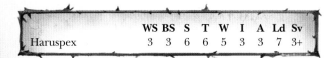

	WS	BS	S	T	W	I	A	Ld	Sv
Haruspex	3	3	6	6	5	3	3	7	3+

UNIT TYPE: Monstrous Creature.

WEAPONS & BIOMORPHS: Grasping tongue (pg 64), **acid blood** (pg 67), **crushing claws** (pg 63).

SPECIAL RULES: Fearless, Instinctive Behaviour (Feed) (pg 38).

Feeder-beast: If a Haruspex inflicts at least one unsaved Wound in the Assault phase, then at the end of that phase it recovers a single Wound lost earlier in the battle.

Rapacious Hunger: In the turn in which a Haruspex charges, every unsaved Wound that it inflicts in close combat immediately allows it to make an additional Attack. These bonus Attacks cannot generate further Attacks. Wounds that inflict Instant Death only generate one bonus Attack. Note that Wounds caused by its Hammer of Wrath, acid blood or tail biomorph do not benefit from this rule.

	WS	BS	S	T	W	I	A	Ld	Sv
Pyrovore	3	3	4	4	3	2	2	6	4+

UNIT TYPE: Infantry.

WEAPONS & BIOMORPHS: Flamespurt (pg 64), **acid blood** (pg 67), **acid maw** (pg 67).

SPECIAL RULES: Instinctive Behaviour (Feed) (pg 38), **Very Bulky.**

Volatile: If a Pyrovore is slain by a Wound that inflicted Instant Death, every unit suffers a Strength 3 AP- hit for each model (excluding Pyrovores) within D6" of the slain Pyrovore (resolve damage before removing the Pyrovore as a casualty).

CARNIFEXES

Carnifexes are living engines of destruction, towering monsters of unyielding armoured chitin and knotted alien musculature. They are one of the toughest and deadliest of all a hive fleet's warrior creatures, created to spearhead assaults in massed battles. Though the Hive Mind has since created larger warrior-organisms, few are the Carnifex's equal in terms of size to strength, nor in terms of sheer destructive potential.

The Imperium's first recorded Carnifex encounters occurred in the battles leading to Hive Fleet Behemoth's invasion of Macragge. As the great star-vessels of Mankind strove with the unearthly living ships of the Tyranids, Carnifexes were to be found at the head of every boarding action, tearing the defenders apart with scythe-shaped talons and immolating the survivors with incandescent bolts of bio-plasma. These creatures swiftly became known as 'Screamer Killers', named for the terrible ululating shriek that accompanied their bio-plasma discharges. Though many other iterations of Carnifex have since been encountered, some even more fearsome by any objective standard, the Screamer Killer had slaughtered its way into legend.

Carnifexes are created by the hive fleets in relatively large numbers, meaning that it is a rare Tyranid assault that does not include at least one brood of these mighty creatures.

They are rugged and adaptable bioforms, their great strength allowing them to wield some of the Tyranids' most powerful weaponry with ease. This allows the hive fleets to create an army of monsters perfectly suited to overcome and destroy a prey world's defenders. To make matters worse, Carnifexes are protected by a heavy, reinforced exoskeleton that is at least as dense as ceramite. Combined with their massive bulk and unnatural alien vitality, Carnifexes can shrug off an obscene amount of firepower and endure horrendous wounds before succumbing to death.

Though Carnifexes lack the swiftness of other creatures in the Tyranid swarm, they more than make up for it in sheer brute force. A Carnifex's thunderous charge starts slowly, steely sinews straining as the beast propels its improbable bulk to top speed making the ground itself shake. Its heavy footfalls beat out a sonorous drum-beat of doom as it strides forth. As the beast reaches full speed, its prey scatters before it or is trampled to death. A charging Carnifex is likened to a living battering ram, for their immense bulk can crush any opponent that bars its way and smash through almost any obstacle. Indeed, only a hardened fortress wall or super-heavy tank has any hope of surviving the impact and stalling the Carnifex's stampede. Sometimes, not even this proves sufficient, as the few surviving records from Macragge's polar fortresses bear testament. The best way to survive a charging Carnifex is to be elsewhere when it arrives.

Fortunately for the other races of the galaxy, the Carnifex is not without a weakness. A Carnifex is a beast of little self-awareness and even less intellect, needing constant supervision by synapse creatures lest it revert to an unthinking rampage that, while horrifying to behold, can be exploited by a cunning strategist. However, whatever solace an enemy general might take from a Carnifex's lack of tactics is unlikely to extend to the troops facing such a monster on the battlefield – even an undirected Carnifex can wreak a path of carnage and havoc before it is eventually brought down.

	WS	BS	S	T	W	I	A	Ld	Sv
Carnifex	3	3	9	6	4	2	3	7	3+

UNIT TYPE: Monstrous Creature.

WEAPONS & BIOMORPHS:
Two pairs of scything talons (pg 63).

SPECIAL RULES: Fearless,
Instinctive Behaviour (Feed) (pg 38).

Living Battering Ram: When this model charges, it inflicts D3 Hammer of Wrath Attacks, rather than just 1.

RIPPER ORGANISMS

From the moment a Tyranid hive fleet makes planetfall, countless voracious organisms are released. Most numerous amongst these creatures are Rippers. They writhe across the surface, their numbers ever growing as they consume everything in their path. Ripper organisms follow hard on the heels of the Tyranid advance, devouring the dead and wounded with grim efficiency and boundless vigour.

During a Tyranid invasion, billions of Ripper organisms overwhelm and consume the defenders. When sated, they throw their own engorged bodies into large digestion pools where they, and the biomass they have feasted upon, are broken down into a thick gruel used to feed the orbiting bioships and eventually create more complex creatures.

Uncontested, Rippers will scour a prey world of every scrap of biomass and every drop of moisture, leaving only an empty and desolate wasteland in their wake.

RIPPER SWARMS

A Ripper Swarm is a writhing mat of maggot-like Tyranid organisms driven by a single voracious appetite. Each Ripper is little more than an armoured serpent, terminating in a broad maw crammed with needle-sharp teeth. They are persistent beings, quite capable of pulling down creatures many times their size. Once a Ripper's jaws tighten around its prey, they stay clamped shut until a mouthful of flesh is torn away or the Ripper is slain. On the rare occasions when the Rippers discover an obstacle that cannot be chewed through, they burrow beneath the obstruction, guided towards the prey by ferocious feeding instincts.

	WS	BS	S	T	W	I	A	Ld	Sv
Ripper Swarm	2	2	3	3	3	2	4	5	6+

UNIT TYPE: **Infantry**.

SPECIAL RULES: **Fearless,
Instinctive Behaviour (Feed)** (pg 38), **Swarms.**

SKY-SLASHER SWARMS

Though Rippers are the simplest Tyranid organisms, different swarms sport variant characteristics. Winged Rippers, known as Sky-slashers, are an increasingly common sight, especially on prey worlds with little or no land mass.

	WS	BS	S	T	W	I	A	Ld	Sv
Sky-slasher Swarm	2	2	3	3	3	2	4	5	6+

UNIT TYPE: **Jump Infantry**.

SPECIAL RULES: **Fearless,
Instinctive Behaviour (Feed)** (pg 38), **Swarms.**

THE PARASITE OF MORTREX

The Imperial fortress world of Mortrex was one of the most heavily defended planets in Segmentum Ultima – a world where fortifications sprouted from every mountainside and bastions punctuated the landscape. For days, when Hive Fleet Kraken attacked, this formidable defence held back the vicious hordes. However, during the tenth day of the invasion, the Imperial Guard defending Mortrex encountered a winged bioform they had never seen before. Without warning, the monster dove towards the human entrenchments, stabbing at the Imperial Guardsmen with lightning-quick strikes of its tail. The creature's victims were thus injected with Ripper parasites, many of which grew to maturity within a few heartbeats, devouring their hosts from the inside out. Amidst agonised death screams, a swarm of Rippers ruptured through cracked bones and torn flesh as they emerged in a spray of blood. The few survivors told of the new Tyranid threat, a horrifying creature that implants organisms into its still-living prey.

They called this creature the Parasite, and all knew that to face it was to risk the most horrific death imaginable. Two weeks later, the planet of Mortrex was overrun by vast, ravenous tides of Ripper Swarms. All that remained was a single transmission that warned of the Parasite.

MAWLOCS

Mawlocs are huge worm-like creatures with great distended jaws. They are the tunnelling outriders to the Tyranid swarm, and burrow deep beneath the ground to bypass a prey-world's front line defences. Once past the outer perimeter, a Mawloc bursts forth in a shower of dirt and stone, swallowing any foes unfortunate enough to be standing where it emerges. The Mawloc then runs rampant throughout the reeling enemy, wreaking as much havoc and carnage as it can with its overmuscled tail before vanishing back below ground once more. Severe tremors are the only warning of a Mawloc attack, making sentry duty on a seismically active world a particularly harrowing experience for the defenders should a hive fleet enter the system.

Physically, a Mawloc is an incredibly simple Tyranid bioform, with little concession given to other roles. Its six clawed limbs are comparatively small and whilst they lack the reach to be especially efficient in combat, they are nonetheless incredibly powerful – employed to gain extra traction whilst burrowing and haul the Mawloc through its tunnels. This should not be taken to mean a Mawloc is defenceless; nothing could be further from the truth. A Mawloc's massive, razor-toothed maw is the entryway to an equally cavernous gullet. Most of the creature's victims are swallowed whole, there to be painfully digested over the course of several days. Those foes large enough to stick in

the Mawloc's craw are first pounded flat by a battery of blows from the creature's muscular tail before being devoured.

A Mawloc is almost entirely blind, and relies on information provided by a series of pressure-sensitive organs that run the length of its flanks. These can absorb and decipher pressure waves, creating a many-layered picture of the world around the Mawloc. It is this ability that allows the creature to hunt its prey even whilst burrowing through the ground. Even the slightest tremor above ground grants a hunting Mawloc a wealth of information, enabling it to intercept a quarry with frightening speed and unerring accuracy. The more regular and rhythmic the sound, the more likely it is that a Mawloc will be able to home in on the source. The pounding thump of a terrified heartbeat is like a flaring beacon to a Mawloc. Thus it is a victim's own fear that betrays their whereabouts and brings about their destruction.

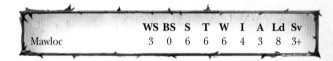

	WS	BS	S	T	W	I	A	Ld	Sv
Mawloc	3	0	6	6	4	3	8	3+

UNIT TYPE: Monstrous Creature.

SPECIAL RULES: Deep Strike, Fearless, Hit & Run, Instinctive Behaviour (Feed) (pg 38).

Burrow: An unengaged Mawloc can, at any point during its Movement phases from the second game turn onwards, elect to burrow. If it does so, remove it from the table and place it into Ongoing Reserves. A Mawloc cannot Deep Strike and Burrow in the same turn.

Terror From the Deep: When arriving from Deep Strike Reserve, a Mawloc can choose to Deep Strike onto a point occupied by another model (friend or foe) – roll for scatter as normal. If a Mawloc Deep Strikes onto a point occupied by another model, do not roll on the Deep Strike Mishap table. Instead, place the large blast marker directly over the spot the Mawloc is deep striking onto. All units except Flyers and Flying Monstrous Creatures beneath the blast marker suffer a number of Strength 6 AP2 hits with the Ignores Cover special rule equal to the number of models that unit has underneath the blast marker. If the blast marker is on a multi-level ruin, only models on the lowest level of the ruin count as being under the blast marker. For Wound allocation purposes, assume the attack is coming from the centre of the blast marker. Hits against vehicles are resolved against their side armour.

If, after removing casualties, it is now possible to place the Mawloc on the table on the spot where the blast marker landed, then do so, even if this is within 1" of another model (but not if it would be in base contact with, or occupying the same space as, another model). If it is not possible to place the Mawloc, replace the large blast marker on the spot and resolve another round of damage as detailed above. If, after removing casualties for a second time, it is still not possible to place the Mawloc, roll on the Deep Strike Mishap table.

TRYGONS

The Trygon is a vast serpentine creature, so colossal that it towers over even the mighty Carnifex. It is a heavily armoured monster, covered from head to tail with a thick carapace of shifting plates. As the Trygon moves, these plates generate a potent bio-static charge that courses along the length of the beast's body and wreathes its bladed forelimbs with crackling power. The Trygon can direct this energy as a lethal high-voltage discharge – unleashing pulsing arcs of lightning that leave its prey as little more than a charred pile of scorched bones.

A Trygon's claws are not only fearsome in close combat, they also allow it to burrow through practically any material. When a Trygon detects an enemy above, it digs upwards, bursting through the ground with explosive force, its huge claws scything through warriors and tanks alike. Such attacks are hard to detect and harder to defend against, especially on worlds with background seismic activity. Once the beast emerges, only focused heavy-weapons fire can be relied upon to bring it down, for the Trygon's iron-hard carapace is proof against all else.

Trygons excavate a massive network of underground tunnels as they burrow beneath the surface of a prey world. Other Tyranid creatures use the passageways left in the Trygon's wake, scuttling unseen as battle rages overhead. The emergence of a tunnelling Trygon therefore often heralds a larger Tyranid attack, with hordes of creatures pouring out of the tunnel shortly after its emergence.

TRYGON PRIMES

As with many Tyranid organisms, different Trygons display substantial variety; one of the most distinct is the Trygon Prime. These beasts have elongated jaws and containment spines running the length of their sinuous bodies, to better harness and direct their bio-electric discharges. More dangerous still, these Trygons share a strong synaptic link with the Hive Mind and are able to dominate the will of lesser Tyranid creatures.

	WS	BS	S	T	W	I	A	Ld	Sv
Trygon	5	3	6	6	6	4	5	8	3+
Trygon Prime	5	3	6	6	6	4	5	10	3+

UNIT TYPE: Monstrous Creature.

WEAPONS & BIOMORPHS:
Bio-electric pulse (Trygon only) (pg 63),
bio-electric pulse with containment spines
(Trygon Prime only) (pg 63),
two pairs of scything talons (pg 63).

SPECIAL RULES: Deep Strike, Fearless (Trygon only),
Fleet, Instinctive Behaviour (Feed) (Trygon only) (pg 38),
Shadow in the Warp (Trygon Prime only) (pg 38),
Synapse Creature (Trygon Prime only) (pg 38).

Subterranean Assault: If, when a Trygon (or Trygon Prime) deploys via Deep Strike, it scatters on top of impassable terrain or another model (friend or foe), reduce the scatter distance by the minimum required to avoid the obstacle.

After the Trygon (or Trygon Prime) has emerged, mark the position under the creature's base with a suitable marker – this represents the tunnel left by its emergence. Any friendly Tyranid Infantry unit that arrives from reserve in subsequent turns may emerge from the Trygon's tunnel instead of arriving from reserve as normal. Only one unit may emerge from each tunnel marker each turn.

If any unit chooses to do so, place the entire unit so that all of its models are wholly within 6" of the centre of the marker and in unit coherency. These models cannot be placed within 1" of enemy models or within impassable terrain; if any models cannot be placed, these excess models are removed as casualties. A unit may not move or charge on the same turn it arrives from a Trygon's tunnel, but may shoot or Run.

HIVE CRONES

The Hive Crone is a flying monstrosity used by the Tyranids to establish air superiority over prey worlds. It is a creature perfectly adapted to aerial combat, able to wrestle enemy aircraft out of the skies as proficiently as any daredevil pilot at the controls of a sophisticated jet-fighter.

A clutch of parasitic tentaclids nestle underneath a Hive Crone's wings, latched on until launched at enemy aircraft. Upon leaving their host, these creatures speed through the air, homing in on their target with unerring accuracy. When these living missiles strike, they emit a massive bio-electric pulse that can cripple the target's electronics or stall their engines, leaving them without power or thrust and sending them into a fatal dive. But even without these impressive bio-missiles to shoot its prey, a Hive Crone is still deadly, flying close enough to its quarry to tear through them with the bladed spurs on its underside. Once all aerial prey has been eliminated, a Hive Crone then softens up the planet's ground-bound defenders, swooping over the heads of the enemy soldiery and drizzling digestive fluids onto its victims.

Before reaching a target planet, Hive Crones also protect bio-ships in their journeys through extragalactic space against attacks from enemy assault shuttles and bomber craft; in silence, a hive fleet's Crones glide through the inky darkness, ripping enemy vessels open to the cold vacuum.

	WS	BS	S	T	W	I	A	Ld	Sv
Hive Crone	3	3	5	5	5	5	3	10	4+

UNIT TYPE: Flying Monstrous Creature.

WEAPONS & BIOMORPHS: Drool cannon (pg 64), **four tentaclids** (pg 65), **scything talons** (pg 63).

SPECIAL RULES: Fearless, Instinctive Behaviour (Feed) (pg 38).

Raking Strike: A Hive Crone's Vector Strike is resolved at Strength 8.

MEIOTIC SPORES

Meiotic Spores are large fleshy sacks full of bio-acid and spore mines. They are mindless beasts, sometimes controlled by the will of synapse creatures, but more often left to drift across a war zone until triggered by an unsuspecting foe.

Though occasionally encountered at ground level, Meiotic Spores most often float high above the battlefield, their trailing tendrils alert for non-Tyranid life. When such prey is detected, the Meiotic Spore vents gas from a series of bladders, allowing it to close with alarming speed. Once the enemy is within range, the Meiotic Spore detonates, showering the area with corrosive juices. The force of this explosion is far greater than that of an ordinary Spore Mine, and is often sufficient to rupture an aircraft's hull. Sensors, ailerons and other more sensitive equipment are almost certain to be destroyed, unless the pilot veers off at the last moment – which is as likely to send the aircraft into collision with another Meiotic Spore as it is to bring salvation. In the first recorded encounter with Meiotic Spores, Space Marines of the Red Scorpions Chapter suffered severe losses to their fleet of Thunderhawk Gunships before they could develop effective countermeasures.

Many of the Spore Mines within a Meiotic Spore are detonated alongside their parent, their demise adding to the force of the already formidable blast. Some, however, are flung free, and continue to drift in search of new targets – which normally transpire to be any crew or passengers who have bailed out of the doomed aircraft. Thus is the threat of a Meiotic Spore often not ended simply by shooting it down.

HARPIES

Harpies are monstrous bioforms that fly with a deftness and agility unattainable by even the most sophisticated fighter-craft. As they soar overhead, they rain clusters of living bombs onto prey worlds whilst their forearms, which are melded with large bio-weapons, spit death as they fly.

Harpies appear in the early stages of a Tyranid attack, working in concert with Gargoyles to drive prey creatures out into the open. However, though the two species share a similar goal, they are physically very different. Where the Gargoyle is very much akin to a winged Termagant, the Harpy appears much closer in nature to a Trygon.

As with many of the larger Tyranid bioforms, the Harpy utilises a wide array of weaponry, according to the particular tactical needs of the hive fleet. In addition to the bloated Spore Mine cysts on their undersides and the bio-weapons fused to their forearms, the ribcages of many Harpies conceal rows of barbed spines. These are typically fired as the Harpy flies over the foe, ripping through infantry formations below.

However, the Harpy is most feared for the ear-splitting shriek that it makes as it dives for the kill. Such is the pitch and volume of this piercing noise that it is almost a weapon in itself. It is excruciatingly painful to lesser life forms, such as Orks and humans, and can even prove fatal to creatures with more highly developed senses, such as Eldar or the genetically enhanced Space Marines. Those that survive this cacophonous assault are left dizzied and disoriented, easy prey for the Harpy's razor-sharp talons.

Perhaps due to its opportunistic nature, the Harpy tends to avoid protracted assaults, instead opting for strafing runs performed at the nadir of one of its swooping dives. This is not to say that the Harpy does not engage in bloody melee, but it rarely engages in such a contest unless the odds of victory are stacked in its favour. Accordingly, the Harpy's favoured quarry is something ill-suited to fighting back – light enemy vehicles are a particular favourite, as they lack the speed to escape and the capacity to offer any real threat to the Harpy at short range.

	WS	BS	S	T	W	I	A	Ld	Sv
Harpy	3	3	5	5	5	5	3	10	4+

UNIT TYPE: Flying Monstrous Creature.

WEAPONS & BIOMORPHS:
Twin-linked stranglethorn cannon (pg 63),
scything talons (pg 63), **spore mine cysts** (pg 65).

SPECIAL RULES: Fearless,
Instinctive Behaviour (Hunt) (pg 38).

Sonic Screech: When a Harpy charges into combat, all enemy models in the combat suffer -5 to their Initiative (to a minimum of 1) until the end of that Assault phase.

HARRIDANS

Harridans are truly massive creatures, likened to the flying drakes and wyverns of ancient legend. They are the largest Tyranid bioform capable of atmospheric flight, soaring through a prey world's skies on vast, leathery wings. Though they lack the sheer speed of an attack aircraft, it is a brave fool indeed who thinks them an easy target. Harridans can slice a flyer apart with a single swipe of their massive talons. More impressive still is the Harridan's endurance, for it can remain aloft indefinitely and need never land. Harridans act as brood mothers for the smaller Gargoyles and their undersides writhe with teeming flocks of them. When the Harridan has transported its broods to their destination, the Gargoyles unlatch their claws and open their own membranous wings, resembling a dark cloud that descends to swallow the prey below.

TYRANNOFEXES

There can be little doubt that the massive Tyrannofex exists purely for destruction – it is a monster created for the most apocalyptic and gruelling of battlegrounds. Striding ominously towards their prey, these alien giants deal death from afar, shattering enemy battle lines with merciless salvos of bio-weapons fire. The only way to stop the unrelenting slaughter is to slay the beast, but a Tyrannofex has the fortitude of a living battle fortress and is heedless of all but the heaviest enemy ordnance. Clad in ablative layers of chitinous armour, a Tyrannofex is as unyielding as any war engine built of steel or born of conventional technology.

Given its enormous bulk, a Tyrannofex is ponderous and prone to being overwhelmed in a protracted melee. Therefore, the Hive Mind rarely unleashes such a creature without at least a brood or more of Termagants to act as close support and defence, allowing the Tyrannofex itself to concentrate on blasting the enemy asunder with its fearsome weapon symbiotes.

'How ironic it is that, as fast as we spread progress and hope throughout the galaxy, the Tyranids spread death and despair.'
- AUN'SHI OF VIOR'LA

A Tyrannofex's weaponry eclipses that of its foes' most powerful battle tanks. Cluster spine launchers nestling within thick armour plates provide the Tyrannofex with a formidable anti-infantry arsenal, but it is for the giant bio-cannon cradled in its forelimbs that this hulking warrior-beast is most feared across the galaxy.

The Tyrannofex's primary bio-weapon is amongst the largest and most destructive to be carried by any Tyranid bioform smaller than a bio-titan. The precise nature of this weapon symbiote is different from creature to creature, ranging from acid sprays that can melt entire infantry formations to giant bio-cannons that can punch holes clean through Space Marine Land Raiders or Necron Monoliths.

	WS	BS	S	T	W	I	A	Ld	Sv
Tyrannofex	3	3	6	6	6	2	3	8	2+

UNIT TYPE: Monstrous Creature.

WEAPONS & BIOMORPHS: Acid spray (pg 63), **stinger salvo** (pg 65).

SPECIAL RULES: Fearless, Instinctive Behaviour (Hunt) (pg 38).

TYRANID BIO-TITANS

Tyranid bio-titans are the most gigantic of all the monstrosities unleashed by the hive fleets during a planetary invasion and are brought into action only against the most determined defences. They are immense creatures, towering over the battlefield and bristling with spines, claws, tendrils and apocalyptic bio-weapons. The most commonly encountered bio-titans unleashed by the hive fleets are the Hierodule and the even larger Hierophant. Though classified as Titans by the indigenous races of the galaxy, these monsters bear little resemblance to the noble war engines of the Adeptus Mechanicus, the graceful wraithbone constructs of the Eldar, or even the idol-like Gargants of the Orks, except in terms of size and lethality.

As with all Tyranid organisms, rapid mutability and adaption is common to bio-titans. Like the hive ships that created them, bio-titans appear to be composites of several different creatures so closely meshed and fused together that they have become an indistinguishable whole. Bio-titans are notoriously difficult to kill, even with super-heavy weaponry. They are protected by ridged plates of chitin that are angled to deflect incoming blasts. Even if this exterior is penetrated, the composite nature of these behemoths means that a fatal injury to one symbiote is unlikely to slay the bio-titan as a whole. Only the focussed and repeated firepower of an enemy Titan, or the combined ordnance of an entire army, have a hope of destroying a bio-titan. Whether such arms can bring the bio-titan down before it rips the enemy battle line to shreds is another question entirely...

THE SWARMLORD

Amongst the billions of creatures created by the Hive Mind, there exists one as old as the Tyranid race itself. This creature is the very pinnacle of the Hive Tyrant bioform, the ultimate conduit through which the Hive Mind's implacable will is enforced. This creature is to a Hive Tyrant what a Hive Tyrant is to a Termagant. It is a monster of darkest nightmare that has preyed on empires and overseen the extinction of entire civilisations. It is a legendary destroyer of worlds and its names are legion. It is the Tyrantlord of the Hive Mind, the Herald of Great Devourer and the Destroyer of the Kha'la Empire. To the Imperium of Man, the latest to face this ancient predator, it is the Swarmlord, and it represents the greatest Tyranid threat to the galaxy.

Since the First Tyrannic War, the Swamlord has carved a bloody path of carnage across the galaxy. It was responsible for the Scouring of the Megyre System, the destruction of the Brynarr race and the consumption of Waaagh! Gorgluk. Not only did these events span several centuries, but each was perpetrated by a different hive fleet. It would therefore appear that the Swarmlord's link with the Hive Mind transcends normal physical limitations. If the Swarmlord perishes on the battlefield, the Hive Mind re-absorbs its consciousness through the synaptic web. The Swarmlord is therefore deathless, and can be re-grown to face the enemy again, returning each time stronger than ever before.

The reincarnation of the Swarmlord appears to be a stress-induced response by the hive fleets, one triggered when its prey cannot be defeated through biological adaptations alone. Indeed, each time it has been reborn, the Swarmlord has been created with the express purpose of out-thinking the enemy and developing new strategies to achieve the greatest results with the warrior-beasts fighting around it. To this end, the Swarmlord possesses more autonomy than any other Tyranid creature yet witnessed. The Swarmlord combines its own resourcefulness with tactical knowledge and experience accumulated through aeons of bloodshed. Such is the Swarmlord's alien cunning that, on several occasions during the Battle for Macragge, it was able to outmanoeuvre and outwit the Ultramarines, warriors whose own tactical acumen is legendary.

	WS	BS	S	T	W	I	A	Ld	Sv
The Swarmlord	9	4	6	6	5	6	4	10	3+

UNIT TYPE: Monstrous Creature (Character).

WARLORD TRAIT: Synaptic Lynchpin (pg 38).

SPECIAL RULES: Psyker (Mastery Level 3), Shadow in the Warp (pg 38), **Synapse Creature** (pg 38).

Alien Cunning: Whilst the Swarmlord is alive, you must add 1 to your Reserve Rolls.

Swarm Leader: At the beginning of your turn, choose either the Swarmlord's unit, or one friendly unit from *Codex: Tyranids* within 18" of the Swarmlord. Then, choose one of the following special rules: Furious Charge, Monster Hunter, or Preferred Enemy. The chosen unit has that special rule until the end of the turn.

PSYKER: The Swarmlord generates its psychic powers from the **Powers of the Hive Mind** (pg 69).

BIO-ARTEFACTS

Bone Sabres: *The Swarmlord wields two pairs of serrated bone sabres. Through the core of each blade lies a crystalline growth. These alien crystals are not indigenous to this galaxy, and the bone sabres crackle with lethal power.*

The Swarmlord has two pairs of bone sabres. Each pair counts as a Melee weapon with the following profile:

Range	S	AP	Type
-	User	2	Melee, Blade Parry, Instant Death

Blade Parry: The Swarmlord has a 4+ invulnerable save against Wounds caused by Melee weapons.

OLD ONE EYE

The Carnifex known as Old One Eye is a monster of living legend. When Hive Fleet Behemoth descended upon the cavern world of Calth, Old One Eye spearheaded the Tyranid assault. Stampeding through the defenders, it swatted aside Imperial Guardsmen and Leman Russ Battle Tanks as if they were naught but bothersome insects. Only the most powerful of weaponry slowed the beast down and, to this day, its body bears the scars of the many blows that should by all rights have killed it. Foremost amongst these is a deep burn running across its armoured skull, a testament to the courage of a long-forgotten hero of the Imperium who fired a plasma pistol through one of the beast's eyes and into its brain. It was this very shot that brought the Carnifex's rampage to a dramatic halt, the first time such a feat had ever occurred.

The legend of Old One Eye might have ended there had it not been for a band of smugglers who stumbled across the monster's frozen body decades later. Hoping to reap a bounty for the corpse, they thawed the Carnifex out, but even as they did so, its grievous wounds began to heal. Isolated from the guiding presence of the Hive Mind, Old One Eye awoke with only the need to kill. Its one remaining eye gazed hungrily upon the unsuspecting smugglers who barely had time to register the beast was alive before they were slaughtered.

Released from its icy prison, Old One Eye roamed across the blizzard-swept landscape of Calth in search of more prey. Like much of the Ultramar system at this time, Termagants and Genestealers still lurked within caves there, despite Hive Fleet Behemoth's defeat. These creatures were drawn to Old One Eye, sensing in the Carnifex a powerful alpha leader. All over the planet, land convoys were destroyed, hab-domes smashed and entire populations massacred and devoured.

Calth's cries for help did not go unheeded; Sergeant Telion of the Ultramarines, a veteran of the First Tyrannic War, answered them. It did not take the Scout Sergeant long to track his quarry, but neither bolt shell nor knife-blade could pierce Old One Eye's armoured hide. As Telion's warriors were crushed to a pulp beneath the Carnifex's massive claws, the Sergeant somehow managed a one-in-a-million shot that found the pit of its ruined eye-socket. The mighty Carnifex howled in pain and, in its frenzied rage, stumbled into a cavernous ravine. Though Telion led a week-long search for the beast's body, it was never found.

Since that time, there have been scattered reports of Old One Eye re-emerging to wreak havoc, only to be felled through the actions of a bold hero. Indeed, if all the tales are true, Old One Eye has been slain more than a dozen times, but at great cost on each occasion. None know of Old One Eye's true fate; there are those that believe the creature is long dead and that the tales of its return are mere stories to frighten disobedient children. However, rumours persist that creatures matching Old One Eye's description have been seen plaguing planets across Ultramar and beyond. If this is the same creature, it is unknown how it escaped the confines of Calth, but the fact remains that, wherever Old One Eye is sighted, carnage and slaughter follow in its wake.

	WS	BS	S	T	W	I	A	Ld	Sv
Old One Eye	3	3	10	6	4	2	4	8	3+

UNIT TYPE: Monstrous Creature (Character).

WARLORD TRAIT: Adaptive Biology (pg 38).

WEAPONS & BIOMORPHS: Crushing claws (pg 63), **scything talons** (pg 63), **regeneration** (pg 67), **thresher scythe** (pg 67).

SPECIAL RULES: Instinctive Behaviour (Feed) (pg 38), **Fearless, Living Battering Ram** (pg 52).

Alpha Leader: Any friendly unit within 12" of Old One Eye can choose to use Old One Eye's Leadership for any Morale or Leadership tests they are required to make.

Berserk Rampage: For every successful To Hit roll that Old One Eye makes in close combat (excluding those from its thresher scythe), it may immediately make one additional Attack against the same unit. These additional Attacks do not confer extra Attacks.

DEATHLEAPER

Of all Mankind's phobias, it is the unknown and the unseen that commands the greatest fear. The pious people of St. Caspalen came to know such fear because of a single Tyranid organism, a solitary Lictor of such ruthless efficiency that many believed it was in fact a Daemon sent to punish them. So apt at avoiding detection was this predator that the first its victims knew of its presence was when clawed talons plunged into their back. All across the missionary world, watchguards and sentries mysteriously vanished, only to be found days later lying face down in the dirt with their skulls pierced and their brains sucked out. Before long, the soldiers of the St. Caspalen defence force were jumping at every shadow, frightened by any mysterious sound and advancing only with wary trepidation on their patrols, their fears heightened by the unseen beast that hunted them and the grisly death that awaited them. The scared soldiers of St. Caspalen named this predator in a vain attempt to salve their fears, a name uttered only in hushed whispers – they called it Deathleaper.

The rumours of Deathleaper spread like wildfire through the superstitious populace, and with each telling, the tales of carnage grew. That Deathleaper was created as Hive Fleet Leviathan's ultimate assassin seemed clear, but who the Lictor was seeking out remained elusive. This only increased people's anxiety; after all, it could be after them! However, Deathleaper was far more than just a mindless assassin; this is a task any Lictor can perform. Deathleaper was created to be a terror weapon, one crafted to utterly undermine the enemy's morale and break their will to oppose the swarm.

On St. Caspalen, Deathleaper instinctively sensed that the execution of the planet's spiritual leader, Cardinal Salem, would have only accomplished the creation of a martyr, steeling the resolve of the St. Caspalen people in the face of the approaching hive fleet. Instead, Deathleaper infiltrated the Cardinal's cathedral-bunker and slaughtered his advisors, hacked through his bodyguard, and left only the prey-leader himself unharmed, covered in the blood and viscera of his closest aides. Like a monstrous predator toying with a mouse, Deathleaper repeated this gruesome carnage for ten days, bypassing the ever-increasing levels of security each time to come within a claw's grasp of the Cardinal before mysteriously fleeing from the bloody scene. The knowledge that the Tyranid assassin could eliminate him at any time was more than the Cardinal's sanity could take. His daily broadcasts became increasingly frantic, and his panic-stricken paranoia and broken mind did more to break the morale of the St. Caspalen defence forces than any mere execution could have. As terror and confusion reigned free, Hive Fleet Leviathan invaded and the swarm butchered its leaderless prey due solely to the actions of the Deathleaper.

> *'It's there, I know it is, lurking in the shadows, stalking me like an animal. It's death itself I tell you, just watching me, waiting… Oh blessed Emperor, why won't it just kill me?'*
> – THE RAVINGS OF CARDINAL SALEM

	WS	BS	S	T	W	I	A	Ld	Sv
Deathleaper	9	3	6	4	3	7	4	10	5+

UNIT TYPE: Infantry (Character).

WARLORD TRAIT: Mind Eater (pg 38).

WEAPONS & BIOMORPHS: Rending claws (pg 63), **scything talons** (pg 63), **flesh hooks** (pg 67).

SPECIAL RULES: Chameleonic Skin (pg 44), **Deep Strike, Fear, Fleet, Hit & Run, Infiltrate, Instinctive Behaviour (Lurk)** (pg 38), **Move Through Cover, Pheromone Trail** (pg 44), **Stealth, Very Bulky.**

'It's after me!': Nominate an enemy character at the beginning of the game and roll a D3. Whilst Deathleaper is alive, that model's Leadership is reduced by the result.

'Where is it?': Enemy models can only fire Snap Shots when targeting Deathleaper.

WEAPONS AND BIOMORPHS

This section of *Codex: Tyranids* lists the weapons and biomorphs used by the Tyranid hive fleets along with the rules for using them in your games of Warhammer 40,000. Unique weapons and biomorphs carried by named characters are detailed in the appropriate entry in the Forces of the Hive Mind section, while weapons and biomorphs used by all the other types of units are detailed here.

MELEE WEAPONS

> **Designer's Note:** *Tyranid Melee weapons come as pairs. For game purposes, each pair is treated as a single Melee weapon. This means that Tyranid models must fight with two pairs of any Tyranid Melee weapons to gain a bonus Attack in close combat for fighting with two weapons. For example, a Hormagaunt armed with a single pair of scything talons does not gain a bonus Attack, but a Ravener with two pairs of scything talons, or a Genestealer with a pair of rending claws and a pair of scything talons, does.*

BONESWORDS

Boneswords are living monomolecular blades that can drain the life-force of their victims.

Range	S	AP	Type
-	User	3	Melee, Life Drain

Life Drain: Any To Wound roll of a 6 made by this weapon has the Instant Death special rule.

CRUSHING CLAWS

The obscene strength of these claws allows them to smash any foe.

Range	S	AP	Type
-	+1	2	Melee, Armourbane, Unwieldy

LASH WHIPS

Lash whips are cords of muscle that move at lightning speeds to slash their prey.

Range	S	AP	Type
-	User	-	Melee, Swiftstrike

Swiftstrike: A model attacking with this weapon has a +3 bonus to its Initiative during the Fight sub-phase.

LASH WHIP AND BONESWORD

Some Tyranid creatures wield these bio-weapons as a deadly symbiotic combination.

Range	S	AP	Type
-	User	3	Melee, Life Drain, Swiftstrike

RENDING CLAWS

The diamond-hard tips of these claws can tear through armour.

Range	S	AP	Type
-	User	5	Melee, Rending

SCYTHING TALONS

Scything talons are long, razor-edged claws of serrated chitin.

Range	S	AP	Type
-	User	6	Melee

RANGED WEAPONS

ACID SPRAY

This weapon sprays caustic digestive fluids that reduce its victims to shapeless gobbets of liquefied flesh.

Range	S	AP	Type
Template	6	4	Assault 1, Torrent

BARBED STRANGLER WEAPONS

These weapons fire seed pods that grow to maturity in seconds, spreading out hooked tendrils in all directions.

	Range	S	AP	Type
Barbed strangler	36"	4	5	Assault 1, Large Blast, Pinning
Stranglethorn cannon	36"	6	5	Assault 1, Large Blast, Pinning

BIO-ELECTRIC PULSE WEAPONS

As a Trygon moves, it generates a potent bio-static field that discharges with lethal effect when the Trygon sights prey. Trygon Primes have curved spines sprouting from their bodies which contain and amplify this energy.

	Range	S	AP	Type
Bio-electric pulse	12"	5	5	Assault 6
Bio-electric pulse with containment spines	18"	5	5	Assault 12

BIO-PLASMA

Some Carnifexes can generate a roaring ball of bio-plasma within their bodies and vomit forth the resultant energy as an incandescent gobbet of fire.

	Range	S	AP	Type
Bio-plasma	12"	7	2	Assault 1, Blast

BIO-PLASMIC CANNON

This giant weapon can channel bio-plasma through a series of different ventricles to ensure the destruction of its prey, unleashing a vast ball of roaring energy through its central chamber, or firing several focussed streams of death through its surrounding barrels.

	Range	S	AP	Type
Blast	24"	7	2	Assault 1, Large Blast
Streams	24"	7	2	Assault 6

CLUSTER SPINES

Some Tyranid bioforms have rows of quills imbedded in their carapaces that they can project a considerable distance.

Range	S	AP	Type
18"	5	-	Assault 1, Large Blast

DEATHSPITTER

This multi-creature symbiote fires maggot-like organisms with corrosive innards. A spider-jawed set of fangs drags an organism from the weapon's brooding chamber and strips off its shell, before the deathspitter reacts to the caustic flesh with a spasm, firing the maggot to explode in a shower of caustic slime against its target.

Range	S	AP	Type
18"	5	5	Assault 3

DEVOURER WEAPONS

These weapons fling worm-like parasites that burrow into their victim's flesh and eat their way through its nervous system to the brain. The devourers wielded by larger Tyranids teem with hives of brainleech worms, a more aggressive and voracious devourer worm.

	Range	S	AP	Type
Devourer	18"	4	-	Assault 3
Devourer with brainleech worms	18"	6	-	Assault 6

DROOL CANNON

Drool cannons fire gobbets of caustic digestive juice over their victims.

Range	S	AP	Type
Template	6	4	Assault 1

THORAX BIOMORPHS

Certain Tyranids have thoracic cavities that play host to swarms of parasites – some of these minute creatures drain their victims' vital fluids, others emit an electrical charge which plays havoc with enemy vehicles, and others still nestle amongst the foe's armour before exploding in a horrific fashion.

Thorax biomorphs are ranged weapons.

	Range	S	AP	Type
Desiccator larvae	Template	1	-	Assault 1, Fleshbane
Electroshock grubs	Template	5	5	Assault 1, Haywire
Shreddershard beetles	Template	3	-	Assault 1, Rending, Shred

FLAMESPURT

The Pyrovore's flamespurt bio-weapon billows forth a blazing plume of fire, engulfing the Hive Mind's foes in a searing conflagration.

Range	S	AP	Type
Template	5	4	Assault 1

FLESHBORER WEAPONS

The fleshborer is a compact brood nest for sharp-fanged borer beetles. When the weapon is fired, a frenzied borer beetle will hurtle itself forward with a single flick of its flea-like legs. The beetle then spends its remaining life energy in a few seconds, frantically boring through the armour, flesh and bone of the first thing in its path. The fleshborer hive is a seething colony for the very same beetles, but the fanged creatures stored in the bloated sacs of the hive lay thousands of eggs that hatch and mature at an astonishing rate within the cavernous chambers of the brood nest. Indeed, the fleshborer hive must eject the beetles at regular intervals to prevent the Tyrannofex from bursting apart due to the mass of creatures birthed within it.

	Range	S	AP	Type
Fleshborer	12"	4	5	Assault 1
Fleshborer hive	18"	4	5	Assault 20

GRASPING TONGUE

This creature's clawed tongue grasps its chosen prey before yanking it bodily into its maw.

Range	S	AP	Type
12"	6	2	Assault 1, Gulp!

Gulp! A To Hit roll of a 6 made with this weapon results in a Precision Shot (see the *Warhammer 40,000* rulebook).

IMPALER CANNON

Impaler cannons propel osseous spines at such high velocities that they can punch through reinforced plasteel. At the base of each spine is a small creature known as a shard-beast that uses thin membranous fins to steer the spine towards its target.

Range	S	AP	Type
24"	8	4	Assault 2, Homing, Ignores Cover

Homing: Impaler cannons can be fired at targets out of the unit's line of sight.

RUPTURE CANNON

This weapon fires two different projectiles, launched in quick succession. The first is a bloated tick that bursts upon impact, showering the target in a thick oily substance. The second, a seedpod, reacts as it contacts the viscous remains of the tick, creating an implosion which can even wrench armoured vehicles inside out.

Range	S	AP	Type
48"	10	4	Assault 2

SHOCKCANNON

Shockcannons fire large claws attached to ropes of sinew, which latch onto their target before delivering a powerful bio-electric surge that electrocutes any prey nearby and disables enemy machinery.

Range	S	AP	Type
18"	5	5	Assault 1, Blast, Haywire

SPIKE RIFLE

This bony, muscle-lined tube launches harpoon-like spikes.

Range	S	AP	Type
18"	3	-	Assault 1

SPINEFISTS

This weapon-creature, typically carried in pairs, has a long tail that burrows through a limb to connect the gun's own air-bladder to the airways and vents of its host. A larger host will exhale great salvoes of spines, ripping through the flesh of anything caught in the blast.

Range	S	AP	Type
12"	3	5	Assault X*, Twin-linked

* Spinefists get one shot for every Attack on the unmodified characteristic profile of the Tyranid creature firing them. For example, a Termagant (1 Attack) fires 1 shot while a Ravener (3 Attacks) fires 3 shots.

STINGER SALVO

Stinger salvoes are simple but effective weapons that fire rows of metre-long, razor-sharp spikes.

Range	S	AP	Type
18"	5	4	Assault 4

STRANGLEWEB

The strangleweb fires a mesh of sticky strands that ensnare the foe, leaving them at the mercy of the approaching swarm.

Range	S	AP	Type
Template	2	-	Assault 1, Pinning

TENTACLIDS

These living missiles seek out aerial prey, latching onto their targets with barbed fangs before emitting a massive bio-electrical pulse.

Range	S	AP	Type
36"	5	5	Assault 1, Haywire, Seeking, One use only

Seeking: If a model makes a shooting attack with this weapon against either a Zooming Flyer or a Swooping Flying Monstrous Creatures, it re-rolls failed To Hit rolls made with this weapon.

VENOM CANNON WEAPONS

These powerful bio-weapons fire salvoes of corrosive crystals at tremendous velocities which shatter on impact to shred the foe.

	Range	S	AP	Type
Venom cannon	36"	6	4	Assault 1, Blast
Hvy venom cannon	36"	9	4	Assault 1, Blast

SPORE MINE WEAPONS

These weapons seed the battlefield with explosive Spore Mines.

	Range	S	AP	Type
Spore Mine cysts	-	4	4	Assault 1, Barrage, Large Blast, Spore Bomb, Spore Burst
Spore Mine launcher	48"	4	4	Assault 1, Barrage, Large Blast, Spore Burst

Spore Bomb: Unlike other weapons, Spore Mine cysts are used during the Movement phase. A Harpy can fire its Spore Mine cysts once in each of its Movement phases. If it does so, it counts as having fired one weapon in its following Shooting phase; however, any other weapons it fires that turn can choose a different target to the Spore Mine cysts. To fire the Spore Mine cysts, the Harpy must be Swooping. After the Harpy has finished moving, centre the large blast marker on any one model the Harpy has passed over that turn and scatter it D6". Units take a hit for each model that is even partially under the blast marker's final position, resolved using the profile above.

Spore Burst: If, when the final position of the first blast marker in the barrage is determined, there are no models (friend or foe) under it, place D3 Spore Mine models anywhere under the blast marker so that they are in unit coherency and not within impassable terrain or 1" of an enemy model (any that cannot be placed are lost). These act as a Spore Mine Cluster for the rest of the game.

	WS	BS	S	T	W	I	A	Ld	Sv
Spore Mine	-	-	1	1	1	1	-	1	-

UNIT TYPE: Infantry.

SPECIAL RULES: Fearless, Deep Strike.

Floating Death: Spore Mines move 3" in the Movement phase and, when they Run or charge, move half the distance rolled. Spore Mines are never slowed by difficult terrain, but must take Dangerous Terrain tests as normal.

Spore Mines do not attack in close combat. Instead, at the Initiative 10 step, the entire cluster detonates! To resolve this, centre the large blast marker over any one of the unit's Spore Mines. Every other unit (friend or foe) under the blast marker suffers a number of hits equal to the number of its models under the blast marker. The Strength of these hits is equal to 4, but is increased by 1 for each additional Spore Mine in the detonating cluster (to a maximum of Strength 10). These hits are resolved at AP4 and ignore cover saves. Once all hits have been resolved, remove all models in the Spore Mine Cluster from play as casualties.

Living Bomb: Spore Mine Clusters are non-scoring, non-denial units. They do not award Victory Points when destroyed, and Wounds suffered by Spore Mines in close combat (including those caused by a Floating Death detonation) are not counted when determining assault results.

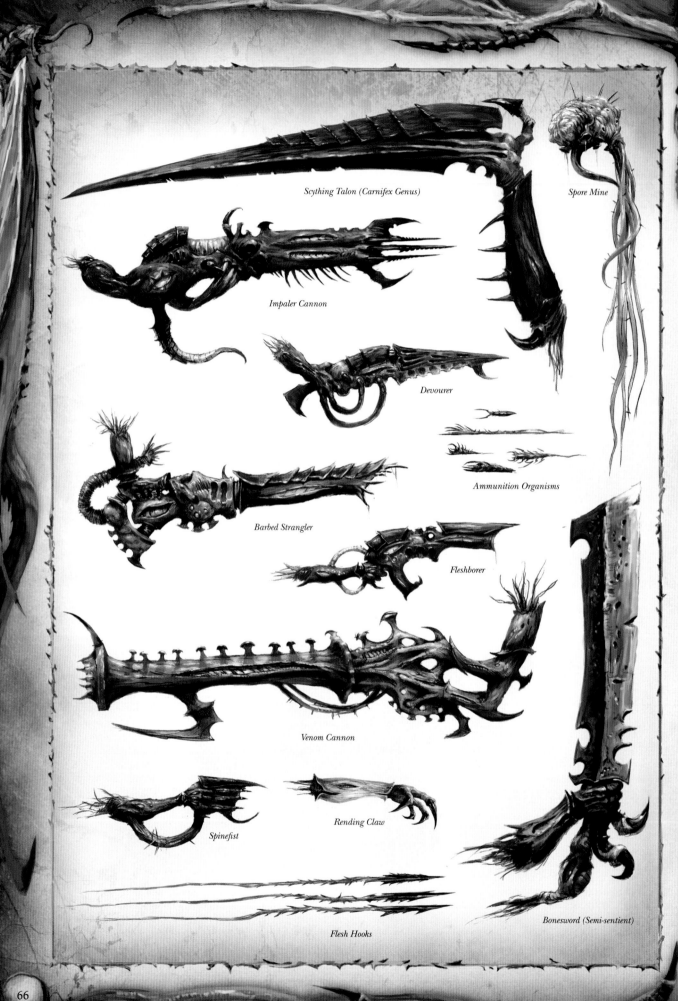

Scything Talon (Carnifex Genus)

Spore Mine

Impaler Cannon

Devourer

Barbed Strangler

Ammunition Organisms

Fleshborer

Venom Cannon

Spinefist

Rending Claw

Bonesword (Semi-sentient)

Flesh Hooks

BIOMORPH UPGRADES

ACID BLOOD

The alien blood spilt from certain Tyranids is so corrosive that it can eat through ceramite armour and dissolve flesh in mere moments.

For each unsaved Wound a model with the acid blood biomorph suffers in close combat, the enemy unit that inflicted the Wound must take an Initiative test at the end of the current Initiative step. For each test that is failed, the unit that inflicted the Wound immediately suffers a Strength 5 AP2 hit with the Ignores Cover special rule.

ACID MAW

The maws of some Tyranids constantly drip with acidic bile.

In close combat, a model with this biomorph can exchange all of its normal Attacks to make a single acid maw attack with the following profile:

Range	S	AP	Type
-	5	2	Melee

ADRENAL GLANDS

Adrenal glands saturate their host's bodies with chemicals that boost the creature's metabolism to a hyperactive state of frenzy.

A model with the adrenal glands biomorph has the Fleet and Furious Charge special rules.

BLINDING VENOM

Some Tyranids spit caustic venom at their prey's eyes.

In close combat, a model with this biomorph can exchange all of its normal Attacks to make a single blinding venom attack, which uses the following profile:

Range	S	AP	Type
-	3	-	Melee, Blind, Poisoned (6+)

REGENERATION

Some Tyranids have the ability to recover from horrendous wounds and injuries that should have proven fatal.

At the end of each friendly turn, roll a D6 for each model with the regeneration biomorph that has less than its starting number of Wounds, but has not been removed as a casualty. On a 4+, that model regains a single Wound lost earlier in the battle.

TOXIC MIASMA

Some creatures emit toxins to poison a prey world's atmosphere.

Once per game, in any Assault phase, a unit with this biomorph can unleash its toxic miasma. If it does so, at the Initiative 1 step, all enemy units engaged in the combat suffer a number of hits equal to the number of models from their unit in base contact with any model from the Tyranid unit unleashing the toxic miasma. These hits are resolved at Strength 3 AP- and have the Poisoned and Ignores Cover special rules.

FLESH HOOKS AND SPINE BANKS

Flesh hooks are attached to a Tyranid's ribcage by ropy tendrils and allow it to scale sheer surfaces or snare prey at close range. The explosive spine banks imbedded in the carapaces of some Carnifexes can also be fired at the foe as the Tyranid charges.

Models equipped with either of these biomorphs don't suffer the penalty to their Initiative for charging enemies through difficult terrain but fight at their normal Initiative. In addition, they can each be fired as a ranged weapon with the relevant profile below.

	Range	S	AP	Type
Flesh hooks	6"	User	-	Assault 2
Spine banks	8"	3	-	Assault 1, Blast

TOXIN SACS

These parasitic glands secrete vile fluids, coating the Tyranid's claws, fangs and talons with a lethal variety of alien poisons.

If a model has the toxin sacs biomorph, its close combat attacks have the Poisoned special rule.

WINGS

The forelimbs of some Tyranid organisms are in fact leathery wings.

If a Monstrous Creature has this biomorph, its unit type is Flying Monstrous Creature.

TAIL BIOMORPHS

The tails of some Tyranids are deadly weapons, from bony protrusions dense enough to cave in the side of a tank to stingers containing enough poison to kill whole regiments.

A tail biomorph is a Melee weapon that allows its wielder to make a single additional Attack. Note that this Attack is resolved separately from a model's other close combat attacks and uses the appropriate profile below. Also note that a tail Attack is **not** affected by other Melee weapons, biomorphs, upgrades or special rules belonging to the owning model, or vice versa. For example, a Hive Tyrant with a heavy venom cannon, a lash whip and bonesword, a prehensile pincer and toxin sacs does not gain an additional Attack for fighting with two close combat weapons, nor does its prehensile pincer tail attack have either the Smash or Poisoned special rules.

	Range	S	AP	Type
Bone mace	-	8	-	Melee, Unwieldy
Prehensile pincer	-	6	5	Melee
Thresher scythe	-	4	4	Melee, Rending
Toxinspike	-	1	6	Melee, Poisoned (2+)

BIO-ARTEFACTS OF THE TYRANIDS

The bio-artefacts of the Tyranids are symbiotic organisms of incredible rarity. Only one of each of the following items may be chosen per army – there is only thought to be one of each of these items in existence (or so the indigenous races of the galaxy hope)…

THE MAW-CLAWS OF THYRAX

During the destruction of Thyrax, the dread beast that spearheaded the assault bore a symbiotic pair of fang-lined pincers. These terrible claws tore apart and consumed the bodies of those brave enough to stand against the monstrosity, absorbing their memories and assimilating greater knowledge of its prey.

Range	S	AP	Type
-	User	5	Melee, Assimilate, Rending

Assimilate: If this weapon's close combat attacks cause an enemy model to be removed as a casualty, the model equipped with the Maw-claws of Thyrax gains the Preferred Enemy special rule against all units chosen from the same codex as the model removed as a casualty.

THE NORN CROWN

First named by Inquisitor Kryptman, the Norn Crown is a unique parasitic organism that clings to the armoured crest of the host creature's head with dozens of tendrils. Burrowing needle-like cerebral bores directly into the brain of its host, the Norn Crown forms a neuro-synaptic link that acts as a hyper-conduit for the Hive Mind. Through this abhorrent union, the Hive Mind's indomitable will can pour forth to augment and control the hordes of lesser Tyranids that scuttle in the leader-beast's wake.

A model with the Norn Crown adds 6" to its synapse range.

THE MIASMA CANNON

The Tyranids utilise all manner of bio-weapons, but none that have earned more dread than the Miasma Cannon. Unlike other venom cannons, this weapon fires gobbets of toxin-laden slime so virulent that it reduces squads of soldiers into shapeless puddles of organic goo in seconds. Whether vomiting noxious fluids in great torrents or liquefying targets in gouts of acid, the Miasma Cannon has been responsible for deaths beyond counting.

	Range	S	AP	Type
Miasmic spit	36"	1	4	Assault 1, Blast, Poisoned (2+)
Miasmic spray	Template	1	4	Assault 1, Poisoned (2+)

THE YMGARL FACTOR

The Ymgarl Genestealers have long been a cancerous blight on the worlds of the Imperium. Their insatiable voracity is legend amongst those that have had the misfortune to encounter them and live. Now, dark rumours have surfaced of another Tyranid leader-beast that appears to share the unfathomable adaptability of the Ymgarl Genestealers.

At the start of every Assault phase, a model with the Ymgarl Factor must alter their form into one of the three listed below. The bonus gained lasts until the end of the phase. The same form cannot be chosen in two consecutive turns.

Slashing Claws: The model has +1 Strength.
Tentacled Limbs: The model has +1 Attack.
Protective Carapace: The model's armour save is improved by 1.

THE REAPER OF OBLITERAX

The Reaper of Obliterax was first encountered amongst the re-emergent Tyranid swarms of Hive Fleet Jormungandr. A deadly bio-weapon resembling a bonesword, this sentient blade is commonly wielded alongside a lash whip. The Reaper discharges highly concentrated bursts of destructive energy, and even the lightest blow can result in the blade's target being rent asunder.

Range	S	AP	Type
-	+1	3	Melee, Life Drain, Shred, Swiftstrike

Life Drain: Any To Wound roll of a 6 made by this weapon has the Instant Death special rule.

Swiftstrike: A model attacking with this weapon has a +3 bonus to its Initiative during the Fight sub-phase.

POWERS OF THE HIVE MIND

Many Tyranids are also Psykers. They do not draw power from the Warp in any fathomable way, but rather they harness a fraction of the Hive Mind's gestalt will. This makes no difference for game purposes and these models follow all the normal rules for Psykers – a Perils of the Warp attack they suffer instead represents massive cerebral trauma or synaptic feedback. Tyranid Psykers use the Powers of the Hive Mind, which is treated as a psychic discipline for all rules purposes.

PRIMARIS POWER

DOMINION .... WARP CHARGE 1

The Tyranid uses its prodigious psychic strength to channel and amplify the will of the Hive Mind.

Dominion is a **blessing** that targets the Psyker. Whilst this power is in effect the Psyker adds 6" to its synapse range.

1. CATALYST .... WARP CHARGE 1

Through its synaptic conduits, the power of the Hive Mind reaches out to infuse the organisms under its control, invigorating their systems with such unnatural vitality that they can ignore the most grievous of wounds.

Catalyst is a **blessing** that targets the Psyker's unit and up to one other friendly unit from *Codex: Tyranids* that is within 12". Whilst this power is in effect, the targets gain the Feel No Pain special rule.

2. THE HORROR .... WARP CHARGE 1

The terrifying psychic presence of the Hive Mind radiates from the synapse creature, flooding the minds of the Tyranids' enemies and causing them to quail and panic.

The Horror is a **malediction** that targets a single enemy unit within 24". The target must immediately take a Pinning test (as described for the Pinning special rule in the *Warhammer 40,000* rulebook) with a -2 modifier to their Leadership.

3. ONSLAUGHT .... WARP CHARGE 1

The synapse creature reaches out its mind and seizes control of the lesser creatures' weapon symbiotes, guiding their fire whilst simultaneously driving the swarms towards the enemy at a breakneck pace.

Onslaught is a **blessing** that targets a single friendly unit within 24". Whilst this power is in effect, the target unit can both Run and then shoot in its Shooting phase.

4. PAROXYSM .... WARP CHARGE 1

The Hive Mind debilitates its enemies by triggering every nerve and pain receptor in their bodies, overwhelming their senses with wracking fits of agony.

Paroxysm is a **malediction** that targets a single enemy unit within 24". Whilst this power is in effect, the target unit's Weapon Skill and Ballistic Skill are both reduced by D3 (roll once and apply the result to both characteristics).

5. PSYCHIC SCREAM .... WARP CHARGE 1

Through its vassal, the Hive Mind unleashes a piercing shriek of undiluted psychic energy that shreds the minds of those caught in the wake.

Psychic Scream is a **nova** power with a range of 6". For each target unit, roll 2D6+2 and subtract their Leadership. That unit suffers a number of Wounds equal to the result. Armour and cover saves cannot be taken against Wounds caused by *Psychic Scream*.

6. WARP BLAST .... WARP CHARGE 2

The Tyranid taps into the raw power of the Hive Mind, unleashing it as a blast of pure Warp energy that arcs from its cranium and vaporises its prey.

Warp Blast is a **witchfire** power. *Warp Blast* can be used as either a Burst or a Lance. Each time this power is manifested, the controlling player must choose which profile is being used, before the target is chosen:

	Range	S	AP	Type
Burst	24"	5	3	Assault 1, Blast
Lance	18"	10	2	Assault 1, Lance

'They are coming! I feel them scratching inside my mind, scratching, screaming, running, so many... so, so many voices. They're coming for us – flesh, body and soul!'

Colours of the Hive Fleets

The Tyranids offer collectors and painters a plethora of choices, from swarms of warrior-creatures to hulking alien monsters. All Tyranids within a hive fleet tend to share the same colourings, with weapon symbiotes often contrasting vividly with their host. That said, variances in hue and shade are common, and splinter fleets often display markings that are altogether unique.

The Swarmlord, Herald of the Great Devourer

Tyranid Prime with deathspitter, lash whip and bonesword

Old One Eye is a nigh-unstoppable engine of destruction.

A winged Hive Tyrant takes synaptic command of a Tyranid swarm as Hive Fleet Leviathan sweeps through the ruins of an Imperial city.

Deathleaper

Hive Tyrant with heavy venom cannon, lash whip and bonesword

Tyranid Warriors from Hive Fleet Behemoth, Hive Fleet Kraken and Hive Fleet Leviathan

Tyranid Warrior with venom cannon and scything talons

Tyranid Warrior with barbed strangler and boneswords

Tyranid Warriors are powerful and versatile creatures, able to utilise a wide range of weapon symbiotes.

Tyrant Guard with rending claws and crushing claws

Tyrant Guard with rending claws and scything talons

Tyrant Guard with rending claws, lash whip and bonesword

Hive Guard with shockcannon

Hive Guard with shockcannon

Hive Guard with impaler cannon

A Tervigon can spawn new broods of Termagants to attack its prey.

Tervigon with crushing claws

Termagants from Hive Fleet Behemoth, Hive Fleet Kraken and Hive Fleet Leviathan

Termagants can bear a number of different weapon symbiotes, including fleshborers and spinefists.

Hormagaunts

Hormagaunts are swift predators that leap and bound across the battlefield to run down their prey.

The warrior-organisms of Hive Fleet Behemoth launch their first attack against a prey world.

A Haruspex is a voracious feeder-beast that consumes everything in its path.

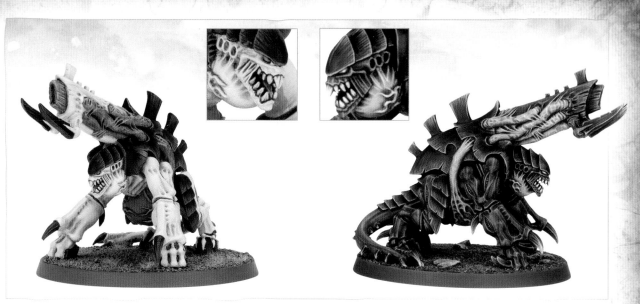

Pyrovores shoot billowing sheets of flame over their prey.

Ripper Swarms from Hive Fleet Behemoth, Hive Fleet Kraken and Hive Fleet Leviathan

Raveners can mount ranged weapon symbiotes within their chest cavities.

The Red Terror

A Mawloc and a Ravener Brood burst forth from beneath the ground to launch a surprise attack.

Prehensile pincer

Trygon

Trygon Primes are monstrous synapse creatures.

An Exocrine mounts a powerful bio-plasmic cannon.

Biovore

Spore Mines

*Carnifex with stranglethorn cannon, scything talons and
bone mace tail*

Tyrannofex with rupture cannon

Cluster spines or stinger salvoes are often embedded into a Harpy's underside.

This Harpy is armed with a twin-linked stranglethorn cannon. These winged monstrosities also drop Spore Mines – living bombs – on their prey as they swoop overhead.

A Hive Crone carries living missiles called tentaclids under its wings, and a drool cannon juts from its fanged mouth.

Gargoyles from Hive Fleet Behemoth, Hive Fleet Kraken and Hive Fleet Leviathan

Broodlords, the most deadly of all Genestealers, with rending claws and scything talons

Genestealers from Hive Fleet Behemoth, Hive Fleet Kraken and Hive Fleet Leviathan

Lictors are deadly Tyranid scouts and assassins.

Zoanthropes channel a fraction of the Hive Mind's psychic might.

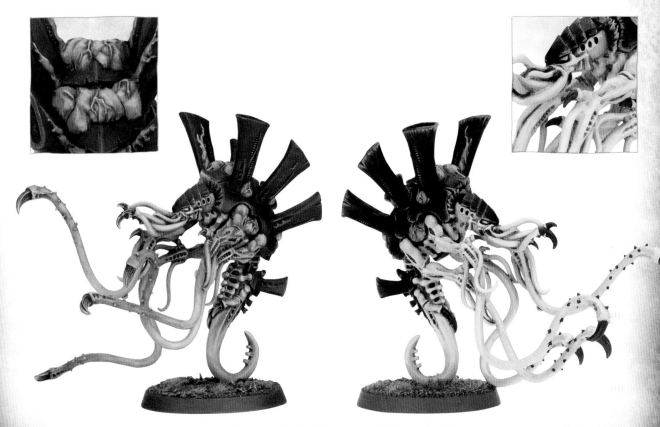

Venomthropes shroud Tyranid swarms in thick clouds of toxic fog.

THE TYRANID SWARM

The following army list enables you to field an army of Tyranids and fight battles using the missions included in the *Warhammer 40,000* rulebook.

USING THE ARMY LIST

The Tyranids army list is split into five sections: HQ, troops, elites, fast attack and heavy support. All of the broods, monsters and unique creatures in the army are placed into one of these categories depending upon their role on the battlefield. Each model is also given a points value, which varies depending on how effective that model is in battle.

Before you choose an army, you will need to agree with your opponent upon the type of game you are going to play and the maximum total number of points each of you will spend. Then you can proceed to pick your army following the guidelines given in the *Warhammer 40,000* rulebook.

ARMY LIST ENTRIES

Each entry in the army list represents a different unit.

More information about the background and rules for the Tyranids and their options can be found in the Forces of the Hive Mind section, while examples of the Citadel miniatures that they describe can be found in the Colours of the Hive Fleets section.

HORMAGAUNT BROOD ①   ① 50 Points

	② WS	BS	S	T	W	I	A	Ld	Sv	③ Unit Type	④ Unit Composition	Page
Hormagaunt	3	3	3	3	1	5	2	6	6+	Infantry	10 Hormagaunts	42

⑤ **Weapons and Biomorphs:**
- Scything talons

⑥ **Special Rules:**
- Bounding Leap
- Fleet
- Instinctive Behaviour (Feed)
- Move Through Cover

⑦ **Options:**
- May include up to twenty additional Hormagaunts..... *5 pts/model*
- The unit may take any of the following biomorphs:
  - Adrenal glands .... *2 pts/model*
  - Toxin sacs.. *3 pts/model*

Each unit in the Tyranids army list section contains the following information:

① **Unit Name:** *At the start of each army list entry you will find the name of the unit alongside the points cost of the unit without any upgrades.*

② **Unit Profile:** *This section will show the profile of any models the unit can include, even if they are upgrades.*

③ **Unit Type:** *This refers to the unit type rules in the* Warhammer 40,000 *rulebook. For example, a unit may be classed as Infantry, Beasts or Monstrous Creature, which will subject it to a number of rules regarding movement, shooting, assaults, etc.*

④ **Unit Composition:** *Where applicable, this section will show the number and type of models that make up the basic unit, before any additional upgrades are taken. If the Unit Composition includes the word 'Unique', then you may only include one of this named unit in your army.*

⑤ **Weapons and Biomorphs:** *This section details the weapons and biomorphs the models in the unit are armed with. The cost for all these models, and their weaponry and biomorphs, is included in the points cost listed next to the unit name.*

⑥ **Special Rules:** *Any special rules that apply to the models in the unit are listed here. These special rules are explained in further detail in either the Forces of the Hive Mind section of this book or the Special Rules section of the* Warhammer 40,000 *rulebook.*

⑦ **Options:** *This section lists all of the upgrades you may add to the unit if you wish to do so, alongside the associated points cost for each. Where an option states that you may exchange one weapon 'and/or' another, you may replace either or both, provided you pay the points cost for each. The abbreviation 'pts' stands for 'points' and 'pts/model' stands for 'points per model'.*

Warlord Traits: *Sometimes an entry will have a specific Warlord Trait, in which case it will be listed here in its army list entry.*

Bio-artefacts: *Some entries have unique bio-artefacts, listed here. These are already included in the unit's points cost.*

WARGEAR LIST

These lists detail the points values of various weapon and biomorph upgrades available to your units. Many unit entries in the army list that follows may include options to select items from one or more of these lists – in each instance, the army list entry will tell you (in bold text) exactly which of these lists you may use.

Basic Bio-weapons .... pg 63-64
A model may replace its devourer with one of the following:
- Scything talons..*free*
- Spinefists ....*free*
- Deathspitter ....*5 pts*

Basic Bio-cannons .... pg 63-65
A model may replace its devourer with one of the following:
- Barbed strangler ....*10 pts*
- Venom cannon ....*10 pts*

Monstrous Bio-cannons .... pg 63-65
A model may replace any pair of scything talons with one of the following:
- Twin-linked deathspitter ....*5 pts*
- Twin-linked devourer with brainleech worms… ....*15 pts*
- Stranglethorn cannon [1] ....*15 pts*
- Heavy venom cannon [1] ....*20 pts*

Melee Bio-weapons .... pg 63
A model may replace any pair of scything talons with one of the following:
- Rending claws ....*5 pts*
- Boneswords ....*15 pts*
- Lash whip and bonesword ....*20 pts*

Biomorphs .... pg 67
A model may take up to one of each of the following:
- Toxin sacs ....*10 pts*
- Acid blood [2] ....*15 pts*
- Adrenal glands..*15 pts*
- Regeneration ....*30 pts*

Thorax Biomorphs...................................... pg 64
A model may take up to one of the following:
- Electroshock grubs..*10 pts*
- Desiccator larvae ....*10 pts*
- Shreddershard beetles ....*10 pts*

Tyranid Bio-artefacts .... pg 68
A model may replace any pair of scything talons with one of the following. Only one of each Tyranid Bio-artefact may be taken per army.
- The Maw-claws of Thyrax......................................*10 pts*
- The Miasma Cannon...*25 pts*
- The Norn Crown [3] ....*40 pts*
- The Ymgarl Factor [3] ....*40 pts*
- The Reaper of Obliterax...*45 pts*

Notes
[1] One per model. A model cannot have both a stranglethorn cannon and a heavy venom cannon.
[2] Cannot be chosen by a Haruspex.
[3] Does not replace the model's scything talons and so can be taken in addition to any other weapon/upgrade.

'Men of the Anarion Fourth, you are the hammer of the Emperor.' Preacher Josef leant forward to grip the podium. 'You are an implacable, unstoppable force. With lasgun and holy flamer, you will descend on the foe like the Emperor's own vengeance.' He paused a moment, allowing his words room to breathe. 'You stand beside your brother soldier as he stands beside you.' Josef raised his fist to the air. 'Together, you will march over the cold corpses of the xenos filth that have infested this world.'

'Lies!'

Josef snapped upright, enraged by the unsolicited interruption. 'Show yourself, wretch! What fool among you thinks it his place to doubt the word of the Emperor?' His eyes narrowed as they scanned the serried ranks of Guardsmen, searching for the malefactor he would soon have put to death.

A man in ruined Anarion fatigues limped onto the muster ground and thrust a bloodied knife at the preacher. 'Lies and false hope,' he spat, grinding the stubs of his teeth together. 'You...' he spun round, gesturing to the ranks of assembled troopers. 'You go to your death.'

'Who are you?' Josef growled at the man, his zealous piety turning to righteous anger.

'Captain Randell. Commander of...' Randell stopped walking, struggling to stay on his feet as his muscles twitched and convulsed. His left arm was missing below the elbow, his skin was blistered and scarred, his eyes barely visible amongst the chewed meat of his face. Thick saliva dripped from his mouth as he spoke, adding to the layers of mud and viscera covering his uniform. 'Last of the Anarion Third.'

'How –' Josef opened his mouth to speak but Randell cut him off with a snarl.

'We cannot win here. The xenos are infinite.' Randell lowered the knife. 'We killed a thousand of them and a thousand more, and still they came. A vile swarm of bone and slick flesh, a...' He stammered, pressing his hand against his ear. 'Chittering, chattering, they came. Hissing and screeching.' Randell sunk to his knees, tears streaming down his cheeks as another spasm wracked his body. 'When they come for you, you will be alone. Your brother will not be beside you, he will not be behind you. He will already be dead.'

HQ

HIVE TYRANT — 165 Points

	WS	BS	S	T	W	I	A	Ld	Sv	Unit Type	Unit Composition	Page
Hive Tyrant	8	4	6	6	4	5	4	10	3+	Monstrous Creature (Character)	1 Hive Tyrant	40

Weapons and Biomorphs:
- Two pairs of scything talons

Special Rules:
- Psyker (Mastery Level 2)
- Shadow in the Warp
- Synapse Creature

Psyker:
A Hive Tyrant generates its psychic powers from the **Powers of the Hive Mind**.

Options:
- May take items from the **Monstrous Bio-cannons, Melee Bio-weapons, Biomorphs, Thorax Biomorphs** and **Tyranid Bio-artefacts** lists.
- May take any of the following upgrades:
  - Indescribable Horror ....*10 pts*
  - Old Adversary ....*15 pts*
  - Hive Commander...*20 pts*
- May take any of the following:
  - Prehensile pincer tail biomorph ....*10 pts*
  - Wings...*35 pts*

THE SWARMLORD — 285 Points

	WS	BS	S	T	W	I	A	Ld	Sv	Unit Type	Unit Composition	Page
The Swarmlord	9	4	6	6	5	6	4	10	3+	Monstrous Creature (Character)	1 (Unique)	59

Bio-artefacts:
- Two pairs of bone sabres

Warlord Trait:
- Synaptic Lynchpin

Special Rules:
- Alien Cunning
- Psyker (Mastery Level 3)
- Shadow in the Warp
- Swarm Leader
- Synapse Creature

Psyker:
The Swarmlord generates its psychic powers from the **Powers of the Hive Mind**.

TYRANT GUARD BROOD — 50 Points

You may include one Tyrant Guard Brood for each Hive Tyrant (including the Swarmlord) in your army. These broods do not use up a Force Organisation slot.

	WS	BS	S	T	W	I	A	Ld	Sv	Unit Type	Unit Composition	Page
Tyrant Guard	5	3	5	6	2	4	2	7	3+	Infantry	1 Tyrant Guard	46

Weapons and Biomorphs:
- Rending claws
- Scything talons

Special Rules:
- Blind Rampage
- Instinctive Behaviour (Feed)
- Shieldwall
- Very Bulky

Options:
- May include up to two additional Tyrant Guard .... *50 pts/model*
- Any model may replace its scything talons with one of the following:
  - Crushing claws...*20 pts/model*
  - Lash whip and bonesword...................................*20 pts/model*
- The unit may take any of the following biomorphs:
  - Toxin sacs..*3 pts/model*
  - Adrenal glands ....*5 pts/model*

OLD ONE EYE — 220 Points

	WS	BS	S	T	W	I	A	Ld	Sv	Unit Type	Unit Composition	Page
Old One Eye	3	3	10	6	4	2	4	8	3+	Monstrous Creature (Character)	1 (Unique)	60

Warlord Trait:
- Adaptive Biology

Weapons and Biomorphs:
- Crushing claws
- Scything talons
- Thresher scythe
- Regeneration

Special Rules:
- Alpha Leader
- Berserk Rampage
- Fearless
- Instinctive Behaviour (Feed)
- Living Battering Ram

HQ

TERVIGON — 195 Points

	WS	BS	S	T	W	I	A	Ld	Sv	Unit Type	Unit Composition	Page
Tervigon	3	3	5	6	6	2	3	10	3+	Monstrous Creature	1 Tervigon	48

Weapons and Biomorphs:
- Stinger salvo
- Scything talons

Special Rules:
- Brood Progenitor
- Psyker (Mastery Level 1)
- Shadow in the Warp
- Spawn Termagants
- Synapse Creature
- Synaptic Backlash

Psyker:
A Tervigon generates its psychic powers from the **Powers of the Hive Mind**.

Options:
- May take items from the **Biomorphs, Thorax Biomorphs** and **Tyranid Bio-artefacts** lists.
- May replace scything talons with crushing claws..................*15 pts*
- May replace stinger salvo with cluster spines..........................*5 pts*

TYRANID PRIME — 125 Points

	WS	BS	S	T	W	I	A	Ld	Sv	Unit Type	Unit Composition	Page
Tyranid Prime	6	4	5	5	3	5	4	10	3+	Infantry (Character)	1 Tyranid Prime	41

Weapons and Biomorphs:
- Devourer
- Scything talons

Special Rules:
- Alpha Warrior
- Independent Character
- Shadow in the Warp
- Synapse Creature
- Very Bulky

Options:
- May take items from the **Basic Bio-weapons, Melee Bio-weapons, Biomorphs** and **Tyranid Bio-artefacts** lists.
- May take flesh hooks..*5 pts*

DEATHLEAPER — 130 Points

	WS	BS	S	T	W	I	A	Ld	Sv	Unit Type	Unit Composition	Page
Deathleaper	9	3	6	4	3	7	4	10	5+	Infantry (Character)	1 (Unique)	61

Weapons and Biomorphs:
- Rending claws
- Scything talons
- Flesh hooks

Warlord Trait:
- Mind Eater

Special Rules:
- Chameleonic Skin
- Deep Strike
- Fear
- Fleet
- Hit & Run
- Infiltrate
- Instinctive Behaviour (Lurk)
- 'It's after me!'
- Move Through Cover
- Pheromone Trail
- Stealth
- Very Bulky
- 'Where is it?'

TROOPS

TYRANID WARRIOR BROOD   90 Points

	WS	BS	S	T	W	I	A	Ld	Sv	Unit Type	Unit Composition	Page
Tyranid Warrior	5	3	4	4	3	4	3	10	4+	Infantry	3 Tyranid Warriors	41

Weapons and Biomorphs:
- Devourer
- Scything talons

Special Rules:
- Shadow in the Warp
- Synapse Creature
- Very Bulky

Options:
- May include up to six additional Tyranid Warriors.... *30 pts/model*
- One model in the unit may take an item from the **Basic Bio-cannons** list.
- Any model may take items from the **Basic Bio-weapons** and **Melee Bio-weapons** lists.
- The unit may take any of the following biomorphs:
  - Toxin sacs.. *3 pts/model*
  - Flesh hooks .... *4 pts/model*
  - Adrenal glands .... *5 pts/model*

GENESTEALER BROOD   70 Points

	WS	BS	S	T	W	I	A	Ld	Sv	Unit Type	Unit Composition	Page
Genestealer	6	0	4	4	1	6	2	10	5+	Infantry	5 Genestealers	43
Broodlord	7	0	5	5	3	7	4	10	4+	Infantry (Character)		

Weapons and Biomorphs:
- Rending claws

Special Rules:
- Bulky (Broodlord only)
- Fleet
- Infiltrate
- Move Through Cover
- Psyker (Mastery Level 1) (Broodlord only)

Psyker:
A Broodlord always knows *The Horror* psychic power.

Options:
- May include up to fifteen additional Genestealers .... *14 pts/model*
- Any model may take scything talons .... *4 pts/model*
- All Genestealers in the unit may take any of the following biomorphs:
  - Adrenal glands .... *2 pts/model*
  - Toxin sacs... *3 pts/model*
- May add a Broodlord ....*60 pts*
- A Broodlord may take items from the **Biomorphs** list.

TERMAGANT BROOD   40 Points

	WS	BS	S	T	W	I	A	Ld	Sv	Unit Type	Unit Composition	Page
Termagant	3	3	3	3	1	4	1	6	6+	Infantry	10 Termagants	42

Weapons and Biomorphs:
- Fleshborer

Special Rules:
- Instinctive Behaviour (Lurk)
- Move Through Cover

The Scuttling Swarm:
For every Termagant Brood of 30 models included in your army, you can include one Tervigon (pg 95) as a troops choice instead of an HQ choice.

Options:
- May include up to twenty additional Termagants .... *4 pts/model*
- For every ten Termagants, one may replace its fleshborer with a strangleweb..*5 pts/model*
- Any model may replace its fleshborer with one of the following:
  - Spinefists .... *free*
  - Spike rifle... *free*
  - Devourer... *4 pts/model*
- The unit may take any of the following biomorphs:
  - Adrenal glands .... *2 pts/model*
  - Toxin sacs.. *2 pts/model*

TROOPS

HORMAGAUNT BROOD — 50 Points

	WS	BS	S	T	W	I	A	Ld	Sv	Unit Type	Unit Composition	Page
Hormagaunt	3	3	3	3	1	5	2	6	6+	Infantry	10 Hormagaunts	42

Weapons and Biomorphs:
- Scything talons

Special Rules:
- Bounding Leap
- Fleet
- Instinctive Behaviour (Feed)
- Move Through Cover

Options:
- May include up to twenty additional Hormagaunts..... *5 pts/model*
- The unit may take any of the following biomorphs:
  - Adrenal glands .... *2 pts/model*
  - Toxin sacs.. *3 pts/model*

RIPPER SWARM BROOD — 39 Points

	WS	BS	S	T	W	I	A	Ld	Sv	Unit Type	Unit Composition	Page
Ripper Swarm	2	2	3	3	3	2	4	5	6+	Infantry	3 Ripper Swarms	53

Special Rules:
- Fearless
- Instinctive Behaviour (Feed)
- Swarms

Options:
- May include up to six additional Ripper Swarms... *13 pts/base*
- The unit may take spinefists .... *4 pts/base*
- The unit may take any of the following biomorphs:
  - Toxin sacs... *4 pts/base*
  - Adrenal glands .... *6 pts/base*
- The unit may purchase the Deep Strike special rule .... *2 pts/base*

ELITES

HIVE GUARD BROOD — 55 Points

	WS	BS	S	T	W	I	A	Ld	Sv	Unit Type	Unit Composition	Page
Hive Guard	4	3	5	6	2	2	2	7	4+	Infantry	1 Hive Guard	46

Weapons and Biomorphs:
• Impaler cannon

Special Rules:
• Instinctive Behaviour (Hunt)
• Very Bulky

Options:
• May include up to two additional Hive Guard .... *55 pts/model*
• Any model may replace its impaler cannon
  with a shockcannon.. *5 pts/model*
• The unit may take any of the following biomorphs:
   - Toxin sacs.. *3 pts/model*
   - Adrenal glands .... *5 pts/model*

LICTOR BROOD — 50 Points

	WS	BS	S	T	W	I	A	Ld	Sv	Unit Type	Unit Composition	Page
Lictor	6	3	6	4	3	6	3	10	5+	Infantry	1 Lictor	44

Weapons and Biomorphs:
• Rending claws
• Scything talons
• Flesh hooks

Special Rules:
• Chameleonic Skin
• Deep Strike
• Fear
• Fleet
• Hit & Run
• Infiltrate
• Instinctive Behaviour (Lurk)
• Move Through Cover
• Pheromone Trail
• Stealth
• Very Bulky

Options:
• May include up to two additional Lictors .... *50 pts/model*

ZOANTHROPE BROOD — 50 Points

	WS	BS	S	T	W	I	A	Ld	Sv	Unit Type	Unit Composition	Page
Zoanthrope	3	4	4	4	2	3	1	10	5+	Infantry	1 Zoanthrope	45

Special Rules:
• Brotherhood of Psykers
• Psychic Brood
• Shadow in the Warp
• Synapse Creature
• Very Bulky
• Warp Field

Psyker:
A Zoanthrope Brood always knows the *Warp Blast* psychic power. The unit can generate one additional power from the **Powers of the Hive Mind**.

Options:
• May include up to two additional Zoanthropes .... *50 pts/model*

VENOMTHROPE BROOD — 45 Points

	WS	BS	S	T	W	I	A	Ld	Sv	Unit Type	Unit Composition	Page
Venomthrope	3	3	4	4	2	3	2	6	5+	Infantry	1 Venomthrope	47

Weapons and Biomorphs:
• Lash whips
• Toxic miasma

Special Rules:
• Instinctive Behaviour (Lurk)
• Poisoned (2+)
• Shrouded
• Spore Cloud
• Very Bulky

Options:
• May include up to two additional Venomthropes ...... *45 pts/model*

ELITES

HARUSPEX

160 Points

	WS	BS	S	T	W	I	A	Ld	Sv	Unit Type	Unit Composition	Page
Haruspex	3	3	6	6	5	3	3	7	3+	Monstrous Creature	1 Haruspex	51

Weapons and Biomorphs:
- Grasping tongue
- Crushing claws
- Acid blood

Special Rules:
- Fearless
- Feeder-beast
- Instinctive Behaviour (Feed)
- Rapacious Hunger

Options:
- May take items from the **Biomorphs** list.
- May take the thresher scythe tail biomorph .... *10 pts*

PYROVORE BROOD

40 Points

	WS	BS	S	T	W	I	A	Ld	Sv	Unit Type	Unit Composition	Page
Pyrovore	3	3	4	4	3	2	2	6	4+	Infantry	1 Pyrovore	51

Weapons and Biomorphs:
- Flamespurt
- Acid blood
- Acid maw

Special Rules:
- Instinctive Behaviour (Feed)
- Very Bulky
- Volatile

Options:
- May include up to two additional Pyrovores .... *40 pts/model*

Fast Attack

TYRANID SHRIKE BROOD 90 Points

	WS	BS	S	T	W	I	A	Ld	Sv	Unit Type	Unit Composition	Page
Tyranid Shrike	5	3	4	4	3	4	3	10	5+	Jump Infantry	3 Tyranid Shrikes	41

Weapons and Biomorphs:
- Devourer
- Scything talons

Special Rules:
- Shadow in the Warp
- Synapse Creature
- Very Bulky

Options:
- May include up to six additional Tyranid Shrikes ...... *30 pts/model*
- One model in the unit may take an item from the **Basic Bio-cannons** list.
- Any model may take items from the **Basic Bio-weapons** and **Melee Bio-weapons** lists.
- The unit may take any of the following biomorphs:
  - Adrenal glands .... *4 pts/model*
  - Toxin sacs .... *3 pts/model*
  - Flesh hooks .... *4 pts/model*

RAVENER BROOD 90 Points

	WS	BS	S	T	W	I	A	Ld	Sv	Unit Type	Unit Composition	Page
Ravener	5	3	4	4	3	5	3	6	5+	Beasts	3 Raveners	49

Weapons and Biomorphs:
- Two pairs of scything talons

Special Rules:
- Deep Strike
- Instinctive Behaviour (Feed)
- Very Bulky

Options:
- May include up to six additional Raveners .... *30 pts/model*
- Any Ravener may exchange one pair of scything talons for rending claws .... *5 pts/model*
- Any Ravener may take one of the following:
  - Spinefists .... *3 pts/model*
  - Devourer .... *5 pts/model*
  - Deathspitter .... *10 pts/model*
- One Ravener Brood in the army may add the Red Terror .... *85 pts*

THE RED TERROR

	WS	BS	S	T	W	I	A	Ld	Sv	Unit Type	Unit Composition	Page
The Red Terror	6	3	5	5	3	5	4	8	4+	Beast (Character)	1 (Unique)	49

Weapons and Biomorphs:
- Two pairs of scything talons
- Prehensile pincer

Special Rules:
- Deep Strike
- Instinctive Behaviour (Feed)
- Swallow Whole
- Very Bulky

SKY-SLASHER SWARM BROOD 54 Points

	WS	BS	S	T	W	I	A	Ld	Sv	Unit Type	Unit Composition	Page
Sky-slasher Swarm	2	2	3	3	3	2	4	5	6+	Jump Infantry	3 Sky-slasher Swarms	53

Special Rules:
- Fearless
- Instinctive Behaviour (Feed)
- Swarms

Options:
- May include up to six additional Sky-slasher Swarms .... *18 pts/base*
- The unit may take spinefists .... *4 pts/base*
- The unit may take any of the following biomorphs:
  - Toxin sacs .... *4 pts/base*
  - Adrenal glands .... *5 pts/base*

FAST ATTACK

GARGOYLE BROOD — 60 Points

	WS	BS	S	T	W	I	A	Ld	Sv	Unit Type	Unit Composition	Page
Gargoyle	3	3	3	3	1	4	1	6	6+	Jump Infantry	10 Gargoyles	42

Weapons and Biomorphs:
- Fleshborer
- Blinding venom

Special Rules:
- Instinctive Behaviour (Hunt)

Options:
- May include up to twenty additional Gargoyles .... *6 pts/model*
- The unit may take any of the following biomorphs:
  - Adrenal glands .... *2 pts/model*
  - Toxin sacs... *2 pts/model*

HARPY — 135 Points

	WS	BS	S	T	W	I	A	Ld	Sv	Unit Type	Unit Composition	Page
Harpy	3	3	5	5	5	5	3	10	4+	Flying Monstrous Creature	1 Harpy	57

Weapons and Biomorphs:
- Twin-linked stranglethorn cannon
- Scything talons
- Spore mine cysts

Special Rules:
- Fearless
- Instinctive Behaviour (Hunt)
- Sonic Screech

Options:
- May replace twin-linked stranglethorn cannon with twin-linked heavy venom cannon .... *5 pts*
- May take one of the following:
  - Stinger salvo .... *10 pts*
  - Cluster spines .... *15 pts*
- May take items from the **Biomorphs** list.

HIVE CRONE — 155 Points

	WS	BS	S	T	W	I	A	Ld	Sv	Unit Type	Unit Composition	Page
Hive Crone	3	3	5	5	5	5	3	10	4+	Flying Monstrous Creature	1 Hive Crone	56

Weapons and Biomorphs:
- Drool cannon
- Four tentaclids
- Scything talons

Special Rules:
- Fearless
- Instinctive Behaviour (Feed)
- Raking Strike

Options:
- May take one of the following:
  - Stinger salvo.. *10 pts*
  - Cluster spines .... *15 pts*
- May take items from the **Biomorphs** list.

SPORE MINE CLUSTER — 15 Points

	WS	BS	S	T	W	I	A	Ld	Sv	Unit Type	Unit Composition	Page
Spore Mine	-	-	1	1	1	1	-	1	-	Infantry	3 Spore Mines	65

Special Rules:
- Deep Strike
- Fearless
- Floating Death
- Living Bomb

Options:
- May include up to three additional Spore Mines.. *5 pts/model*

HEAVY SUPPORT

CARNIFEX BROOD   120 Points

	WS	BS	S	T	W	I	A	Ld	Sv	Unit Type	Unit Composition	Page
Carnifex	3	3	9	6	4	2	3	7	3+	Monstrous Creature	1 Carnifex	52

Weapons and Biomorphs:
- Two pairs of scything talons

Special Rules:
- Fearless
- Instinctive Behaviour (Feed)
- Living Battering Ram

Options:
- May include up to two additional Carnifexes...120 pts/model
- Any model may replace one pair of scything talons with crushing claws ....15 pts/model
- Any model may take items from the **Monstrous Bio-cannons** and **Biomorphs** list.
- Any model may take any of the following:
  - Spine banks...5 pts/model
  - Bio-plasma..20 pts/model
- Any model may take one of the following tail biomorphs:
  - Thresher scythe ....10 pts/model
  - Bone mace ....15 pts/model

BIOVORE BROOD   40 Points

	WS	BS	S	T	W	I	A	Ld	Sv	Unit Type	Unit Composition	Page
Biovore	3	3	4	4	3	2	2	6	4+	Infantry	1 Biovore	50

Weapons and Biomorphs:
- Spore Mine launcher

Special Rules:
- Instinctive Behaviour (Hunt)
- Very Bulky

Options:
- May include up to two additional Biovores ....40 pts/model

TRYGON   190 Points

	WS	BS	S	T	W	I	A	Ld	Sv	Unit Type	Unit Composition	Page
Trygon	5	3	6	6	6	4	5	8	3+	Monstrous Creature	1 Trygon	55

Weapons and Biomorphs:
- Bio-electric pulse
- Two pairs of scything talons

Special Rules:
- Deep Strike
- Fearless
- Fleet
- Instinctive Behaviour (Feed)
- Subterranean Assault

Options:
- May take items from the **Biomorphs** list.
- May take one of the following tail biomorphs:
  - Prehensile pincer ....10 pts
  - Toxinspike ....10 pts

TRYGON PRIME   230 Points

	WS	BS	S	T	W	I	A	Ld	Sv	Unit Type	Unit Composition	Page
Trygon Prime	5	3	6	6	6	4	5	10	3+	Monstrous Creature	1 Trygon Prime	55

Weapons and Biomorphs:
- Bio-electric pulse with containment spines
- Two pairs of scything talons

Special Rules:
- Deep Strike
- Fleet
- Shadow in the Warp
- Subterranean Assault
- Synapse Creature

Options:
- May take items from the **Biomorphs** and **Tyranid Bio-artefacts** lists.
- May take one of the following tail biomorphs:
  - Prehensile pincer ....10 pts
  - Toxinspike ....10 pts

HEAVY SUPPORT

MAWLOC
140 Points

	WS	BS	S	T	W	I	A	Ld	Sv	Unit Type	Unit Composition	Page
Mawloc	3	0	6	6	6	4	3	8	3+	Monstrous Creature	1 Mawloc	54

Special Rules:
- Burrow
- Deep Strike
- Fearless
- Hit & Run
- Instinctive Behaviour (Feed)
- Terror from the Deep

Options:
- May take items from the **Biomorphs** list.
- May take one of the following tail biomorphs:
  - Prehensile pincer .... *10 pts*
  - Toxinspike .... *10 pts*

EXOCRINE
170 Points

	WS	BS	S	T	W	I	A	Ld	Sv	Unit Type	Unit Composition	Page
Exocrine	3	3	6	6	5	3	3	7	3+	Monstrous Creature	1 Exocrine	50

Weapons and Biomorphs:
- Bio-plasmic cannon
- Scything talons

Special Rules:
- Fearless
- Instinctive Behaviour (Hunt)
- Symbiotic Targeting

Options:
- May take items from the **Biomorphs** list.
- May take the thresher scythe tail biomorph .... *10 pts*

TYRANNOFEX
175 Points

	WS	BS	S	T	W	I	A	Ld	Sv	Unit Type	Unit Composition	Page
Tyrannofex	3	3	6	6	6	2	3	8	2+	Monstrous Creature	1 Tyrannofex	58

Weapons and Biomorphs:
- Acid spray
- Stinger salvo

Special Rules:
- Fearless
- Instinctive Behaviour (Hunt)

Options:
- May replace acid spray with one of the following:
  - Fleshborer hive .... *5 pts*
  - Rupture cannon .... *30 pts*
- May take items from the **Biomorphs** and **Thorax Biomorphs** lists.

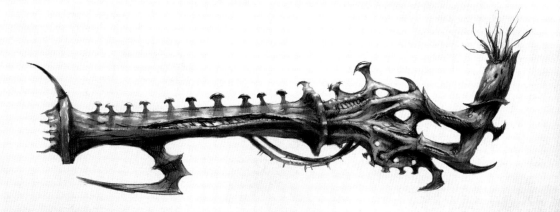

REFERENCE

All of the rules and tables here are condensed for ease of reference. If you need the full rule, see its entry in the main pages of the book.

ARMY SPECIAL RULES (PG 38)

Instinctive Behaviour: At the beginning of each turn, units that are outside the range of friendly Synapse Creatures must take a Leadership test unless they are: engaged in combat, falling back, have gone to ground or arrived from reserve this turn. If they pass, they act normally. If not, roll on the appropriate Instinctive Behaviour table. The result lasts until the beginning of your next turn, unless specified otherwise.

Shadow in the Warp: Enemy Psykers within 12" of this model have -3 Leadership.

Synapse Creature: This model has a synapse range of 12". Tyranid models within this range, including the Synapse Creatures themselves, are Fearless. Units automatically rally if they are within synapse range when they begin their move.

WARLORD TRAITS TABLE (PG 38)

D6	WARLORD TRAIT
1	**Nature's Bane:** At the beginning each of your Movement phases, select a jungle within 12" of your Warlord. It becomes a Carnivorous Jungle for the rest of the game.
2	**Heightened Senses:** The Warlord, and Tyranids within 12" of it, have Night Vision.
3	**Synaptic Lynchpin:** The Warlord's Synapse range is 18".
4	**Mind Eater:** Receive 2 Victory Points for each Independent Character slain by your Warlord in a challenge.
5	**Digestive Denial:** After deployment, one piece of terrain in the enemy deployment zone (but not one your opponent has purchased) has its cover save reduced by one.
6	**Adaptive Biology:** If the Warlord suffers a Wound, it gains Feel No Pain (5+) at the beginning of its next Movement phase.

INSTINCTIVE BEHAVIOUR (LURK)

D6	LURK RESULT
1-3	**Survive:** The unit is treated as having failed a Morale test and must immediately Fall Back.
4-5	**Seek Cover:** In the Movement phase, the unit is not slowed by difficult terrain, though its models must take Dangerous Terrain tests as normal. In the Shooting phase, the unit can Run, but it can only shoot if it is in a building or area terrain (if the unit is partially within area terrain, only those models within area terrain are allowed to shoot). The unit cannot charge in the Assault phase.
6	**Stalk:** See Seek Cover (above). The unit also has Stealth.

INSTINCTIVE BEHAVIOUR (HUNT)

D6	HUNT RESULT
1-3	**Burrow and Hide:** The unit immediately Goes to Ground. Units that contain at least one model with the Fearless special rule treat this result as Prowl (below), instead.
4-5	**Prowl:** In the Shooting phase, the unit cannot Run and must instead shoot at the closest enemy unit that is within range and line of sight. If there is no viable target, the Tyranid unit can do nothing during the Shooting phase. It cannot charge in the Assault phase.
6	**Destroy:** See Prowl (above). The unit also has Preferred Enemy.

INSTINCTIVE BEHAVIOUR (FEED)

D6	FEED RESULT
1-3	**Cannibalistic Hunger:** The unit immediately suffers a number of hits equal to the number of models in that unit. These hits are resolved using the unit's majority Strength (if drawn, use the highest) and AP-. Wounds are allocated by the owning player and armour saves (but not cover saves) may be taken. The unit can do nothing else until the end of its turn. Units of a single model treat this result as Devour (below), instead.
4-5	**Devour:** In the Shooting phase, the unit cannot shoot or Run. In the Assault phase the unit must declare a charge against the closest viable enemy unit; if it cannot, it does nothing in the Assault phase.
6	**Kill:** See Devour (above). The unit also has Rage.

SPECIAL RULES

Alpha Warrior (pg 41): Tyranid Warriors and Shrikes in this unit use the Tyranid Prime's Weapon Skill and Ballistic Skill.

Blind Rampage (pg 46): If a Hive Tyrant in this unit is killed, from the end of that turn the Tyrant Guard have Furious Charge and Rage.

Bounding Leap (pg 42): Run an additional 3" (normally D6+3").

Brood Progenitor (pg 48): All Termagants in units within 12" of the Tervigon have the Counter-attack special rule.

Burrow (pg 54): An unengaged Mawloc can enter Ongoing Reserves during its Movement phase from the second game turn onwards. It cannot Deep Strike and Burrow in the same turn.

Chameleonic Skin (pg 44): Does not scatter when arriving via Deep Strike.

Feeder-beast (pg 51): If a Haruspex causes one or more Wounds in the Assault phase, it recovers a single Wound.

Floating Death (pg 65): Move 3", halve Run or charge moves. Ignore difficult terrain (but still take dangerous terrain tests). Cannot attack: instead, at the Initiative 10 step, centre the large blast marker over one Spore Mine. Models are hit at Strength 4, +1 for each additional Spore Mine in the cluster. These hits are AP4 and ignore cover saves. Then remove the Spore Mine Cluster from play.

Living Battering Ram (pg 52): Has Hammer of Wrath (D3).

Living Bomb (pg 65): Are non-scoring, non-denial units. Do not award Victory Points when destroyed, and do not count towards combat resolution.

Pheromone Trail (pg 44): Friendly units arriving by Deep Strike do not scatter if placed within 6" of this model. This model must already be on the table at the start of the turn for this ability to be used.

Psychic Brood (pg 45): Brotherhood of Psykers with Mastery Level 2. If a Zoanthrope brood uses *Warp Blast*, the number of shots fired is equal to the number of Zoanthropes in that brood.

Raking Strike (pg 56): Vector Strikes at Strength 8.

Rapacious Hunger (pg 51): When it charges, a Haruspex gets a bonus Attack for every unsaved Wound it inflicts in close combat – these do not generate further Attacks. Wounds caused by its Hammer of Wrath, acid blood or tail biomorph do not benefit from this rule.

Shieldwall (pg 46): A single Hive Tyrant (or the Swarmlord) may join this unit as if it were an Independent Character, and automatically passes Look Out, Sir rolls whilst it is part of the unit.

Sonic Screech (pg 57): Enemies have -5 Initiative in the phase in which they are charged by a Harpy.

Spawn Termagants (pg 48): At the end of each friendly Movement phase, you may choose to place 3D6 Termagants (with fleshborers) wholly within 6" of the Tervigon. This unit cannot move or charge this turn, but may shoot or run. If the 3D6 contains a double, the unit is spawned but the Tervigon cannot spawn any further units.

Spore Bomb (pg 65): During the Movement phase, after Swooping, centre a large blast marker on a model the Harpy has passed over; scatter it D6". The Harpy's other weapons can choose a different target.

Spore Burst (pg 65): If no models are hit by this attack, place a Spore Mine Cluster of D3 models under the blast marker before removing it.

Spore Cloud (pg 47): Friendly Tyranid models within 6" of a Venomthrope have Shrouded.

Subterranean Assault (pg 55): Reduce the Trygon's Deep Strike scatter to avoid impassable terrain or models. Mark the final position of its Deep Strike arrival; in subsequent turns, friendly Tyranid Infantry may arrive from reserve from the same point (one unit per turn). Place these units wholly within 6" of the centre of the marker. Models that cannot be placed are destroyed. These units cannot move or charge in the turn they arrive, but may shoot or Run.

Swallow Whole (pg 49): If the Red Terror hits with four or more attacks in a phase (excluding its prehensile pincer), you may nominate a single enemy Infantry, Jump Infantry or Jet Pack Infantry model in base contact. The model must pass a single invulnerable save (if it has one) or be killed. Very Bulky or Extremely Bulky models cannot be Swallowed Whole.

Symbiotic Targeting (pg 50): If an Exocrine does not move, it has +1 Ballistic Skill until the end of its turn. It cannot declare a charge during the same turn that it uses this special rule.

Synaptic Backlash (pg 48): If a Tervigon is slain, all friendly Termagant Broods within 12" suffer 3D6 Strength 3 AP- hits.

Terror from the Deep (pg 54): A Mawloc can choose to Deep Strike onto another model. If, after scattering, the Mawloc is Deep Striking onto another model, place the large blast marker directly onto that spot. Non-flying models hit by this suffer a Strength 6 AP2 hit with Ignores Cover (vehicles are hit on their side armour). Then, place the Mawloc there if you can. If not, resolve another attack as above. If it still cannot be placed, it suffers a Deep Strike Mishap.

Volatile (pg 51): If a Pyrovore is slain by Instant Death, every unit suffers a Strength 3 AP- hit for each non-Pyrovore model within D6" of the slain Pyrovore.

Warp Field (pg 45): Zoanthropes have a 3+ invulnerable save.

BIOMORPH UPGRADES (PG 67)

Acid blood: For each unsaved Wound it suffers in close combat, the enemy unit takes an Initiative test. For each failed test, they suffer a Strength 5 AP2 hit.

Acid maw: Can exchange its normal Attacks for a single Strength 5 AP2 Melee attack.

Adrenal glands: Has Fleet and Furious Charge.

Blinding venom: Can exchange its normal Attacks for a blinding venom attack:

Range	S	AP	Type
-	3	-	Melee, Blind, Poisoned (6+)

Flesh hooks: Ignore the penalty to their Initiative for charging enemies through difficult terrain. Can be fired with the profile below.

Range	S	AP	Type
6"	User	-	Assault 2

Regeneration: Regains a Wound on a 4+ at each turn's end.

Spine Banks: Ignore the penalty to their Initiative for charging enemies through difficult terrain. Can be fired with the profile below.

Range	S	AP	Type
8"	3	-	Assault 1, Blast

Toxic Miasma: One use only. At the Initiative 1 step, enemy models in base contact with this unit suffer a Strength 3 AP- hit with Poisoned and Ignores Cover.

Toxin Sacs: Close combat attacks have Poisoned.

Wings: Becomes a Flying Monstrous Creature.

TAIL BIOMORPHS

A tail biomorph allows its wielder to make a single additional Attack which uses the appropriate profile below.

	Range	S	AP	Type
Bone mace	-	8	-	Melee, Unwieldy
Prehensile pincer	-	6	5	Melee
Thresher scythe	-	4	4	Melee, Rending
Toxinspike	-	1	6	Melee, Poisoned (2+)

POWERS OF THE HIVE MIND (PG 69)

> **PRIMARIS POWER**
>
> ## DOMINION
> **Warp Charge 1. Blessing.**
> The Psyker has +6" synapse range.

1. CATALYST
Warp Charge 1. Blessing.
The Psyker's unit and one other friendly unit from *Codex: Tyranids* within 12" have Feel No Pain.

2. THE HORROR
Warp Charge 1. Malediction.
One enemy unit within 24" must take a Pinning test with -2 Leadership.

3. ONSLAUGHT
Warp Charge 1. Blessing.
A single friendly unit within 24" can Run and then shoot in its Shooting phase.

4. PAROXYSM
Warp Charge 1. Malediction.
One enemy unit within 24" has -D3 Weapon Skill and Ballistic Skill (roll once for both).

5. PSYCHIC SCREAM
Warp Charge 1. Nova.
Range 6". Roll 2D6+2 for each target unit and subtract their Leadership. They suffer a number of Wounds equal to the result, with no Armour or cover saves allowed.

6. WARP BLAST
Warp Charge 2. Witchfire.

	Range	S	AP	Type
Burst	24"	5	3	Assault 1, Blast
Lance	18"	10	2	Assault 1, Lance